MARVEL
UNIVERSE
AN ATLAS OF MARVEL

A STUDIO PRESS BOOK

First published in the UK in 2021 by Studio Press,
an imprint of Bonnier Books UK,
4th Floor, Victoria House, Bloomsbury Square, London WC1B 4DA
Owned by Bonnier Books,
Sveavägen 56, Stockholm, Sweden

www.bonnierbooks.co.uk

1 3 5 7 9 10 8 6 4 2

ISBN 978-1-78741-638-3

Written by Ned Hartley
Illustrated by Jensine Eckwall and David Shephard
Edited by Sophie Blackman
Designed by Rob Ward
Cover designed by Maddox Philpot
Production by Emma Kidd

A CIP catalogue for this book is available from the British Library.
Printed and bound in Italy

Special thanks to: Anthony Cotilleta, Carl Farmer, Mike Fichera, Daron Jensen, Luc Kersten,
Rob London, Chris McCarver, Mike O'Sullivan, Marcus Raymond, Marc Riemer,
Jacob Rougemont, Stuart Vandal, Brian Overton and Joseph Hochstein.

MARVEL
UNIVERSE
AN ATLAS OF MARVEL

FOREWORD

THE UNIVERSE IS A BIG PLACE. THE MARVEL COMICS UNIVERSE IS EVEN BIGGER.

THE ADVENTURES FOUND WITHIN THE PAGES OF MARVEL COMIC BOOKS ARE TRULY EPIC IN SCOPE, BOUND ONLY BY THE WILD IMAGINATIONS OF THE CREATIVE TEAMS WHO BRING THESE ASTONISHING TALES TO LIFE. AND THE LOCATIONS IN WHICH THESE STORIES TAKE PLACE ARE NO EXCEPTION.

MARVEL COMICS HAVE TAKEN READERS ON A TOUR OF THE UNITED STATES OF AMERICA, WITH OUR HEROES AND VILLAINS TRAVELLING, LIVING AND BATTLING FROM COAST TO COAST. WHETHER IT'S LOCATIONS LIKE FOREST HILLS IN QUEENS, NY, WHERE PETER PARKER GREW UP WITH AUNT MAY AND UNCLE BEN, OR GOLDEN GATE PARK IN SAN FRANCISCO, CALIFORNIA, HOME TO THE DREAMING CELESTIAL, MARVEL COMICS HAVE CRISSCROSSED THE UNITED STATES TELLING STORIES OF ACTUAL, REAL-WORLD PLACES FILLED WITH FANTASTIC CHARACTERS AND EVENTS.

THESE STORIES HAVE ALSO CRISSCROSSED THE GLOBE, FROM NORTHERN CANADA, WITH ALPHA FLIGHT, TO THE STREETS OF CAIRO, EGYPT, WHERE ORORO MUNROE ONCE LIVED, TO THE RED ROOM ACADEMY IN RUSSIA THAT CREATED THE BLACK WIDOW PROGRAMME. THROUGH IT ALL, IT WAS IMPORTANT TO BRING THE REAL WORLD – ACTUAL LOCATIONS THAT PEOPLE KNEW, HAD SEEN, TRAVELLED TO OR EVEN READ ABOUT – INTO MARVEL COMICS. THESE LOCATIONS, AND MANY LIKE THEM, HELPED THE STORIES TO FEEL AUTHENTIC AND GROUNDED. IT MADE THEM FEEL REAL. IT ALSO ALLOWED US TO BALANCE ACTUAL SPOTS ON THE GLOBE WITH CREATED ONES, THEREBY LETTING OUR IMAGINATIONS – AND THE IMAGINATIONS OF OUR READERS – RUN WILD. DOING SO ALLOWED FOR THE CREATION OF WAKANDA, THE MOST TECHNICALLY ADVANCED KINGDOM IN THE WORLD; OF LATVERIA, HOME TO

THE SINISTER VICTOR VON DOOM; AND
OF THE SAVAGE LAND, AN AREA DEEP BENEATH
ANTARCTICA THAT HAS BEEN LOST TO TIME.
AND THAT'S JUST THE TIP OF THE ICEBERG.

THE GLOBE IS FILLED WITH REAL AND IMAGINARY
LOCATIONS THAT ALL FEEL LIKE THEY BELONG
TOGETHER ON THE SAME PLANET. OF COURSE,
THAT'S JUST THE EARTH – THERE'S ALSO
OUTER SPACE AND THE TEN REALMS. AND THEN
THERE'S THE ENTIRETY OF THE MULTIVERSE. THE
MULTIPLE LOCATIONS – AND THE WONDROUS
STORIES THAT OCCURRED THEREIN – ARE TRULY
LIMITLESS, AND THAT'S JUST ONE OF THE
GREAT THINGS ABOUT MARVEL COMICS.

YOU HOLD BEFORE YOU A BOOK THAT DETAILS
ALL OF THE MAIN LOCATIONS FROM MARVEL'S
FIRST 80 YEARS. IT'S BOTH A HANDY RESOURCE
AND A THRILLING TRAVEL GUIDE. IT'S ALSO
A GREAT WAY TO REVISIT CLASSIC TALES
AND PIQUE YOUR INTEREST ABOUT OTHER
SENSATIONAL STORIES THAT YOU MAY
HAVE MISSED.

AND ON A PERSONAL NOTE, A BOOK LIKE
THIS WOULD HAVE BEEN ENORMOUSLY HELPFUL
TO MY YOUNGER SELF, WHEN I OVERSAW
THE LIKES OF DAREDEVIL, CAPTAIN AMERICA,
THOR AND SPIDER-MAN, JUST TO NAME A
FEW. A BOOK LIKE THIS REMINDS YOU OF
THE POSSIBILITIES OF COMIC BOOKS, OF THE
ABILITY THAT THEY HAVE TO TRANSPORT YOU
ACROSS THE WORLD – TO REAL AND MADE-UP
LOCATIONS – AND BEYOND.

ENJOY THE JOURNEY!

Ralph Macchio

RALPH MACCHIO
MAY 2021

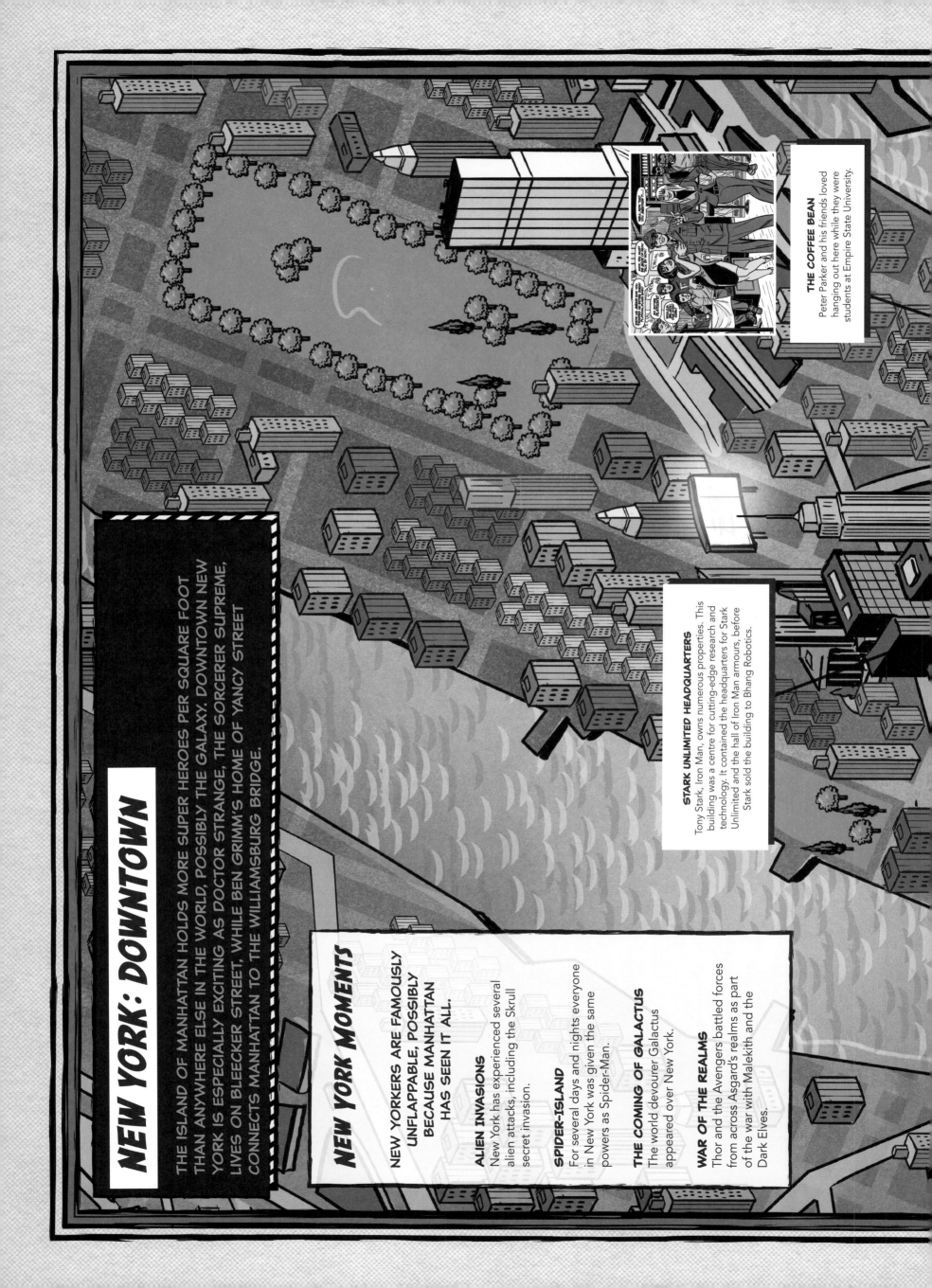

NEW YORK: DOWNTOWN

THE ISLAND OF MANHATTAN HOLDS MORE SUPER HEROES PER SQUARE FOOT THAN ANYWHERE ELSE IN THE WORLD, POSSIBLY THE GALAXY. DOWNTOWN NEW YORK IS ESPECIALLY EXCITING AS DOCTOR STRANGE, THE SORCERER SUPREME, LIVES ON BLEECKER STREET, WHILE BEN GRIMM'S HOME OF YANCY STREET CONNECTS MANHATTAN TO THE WILLIAMSBURG BRIDGE.

NEW YORK MOMENTS

NEW YORKERS ARE FAMOUSLY UNFLAPPABLE, POSSIBLY BECAUSE MANHATTAN HAS SEEN IT ALL.

ALIEN INVASIONS
New York has experienced several alien attacks, including the Skrull secret invasion.

SPIDER-ISLAND
For several days and nights everyone in New York was given the same powers as Spider-Man.

THE COMING OF GALACTUS
The world devourer Galactus appeared over New York.

WAR OF THE REALMS
Thor and the Avengers battled forces from across Asgard's realms as part of the war with Malekith and the Dark Elves.

THE COFFEE BEAN
Peter Parker and his friends loved hanging out here while they were students at Empire State University.

STARK UNLIMITED HEADQUARTERS
Tony Stark, Iron Man, owns numerous properties. This building was a centre for cutting-edge research and technology. It contained the headquarters for Stark Unlimited and the hall of Iron Man armours, before Stark sold the building to Bhang Robotics.

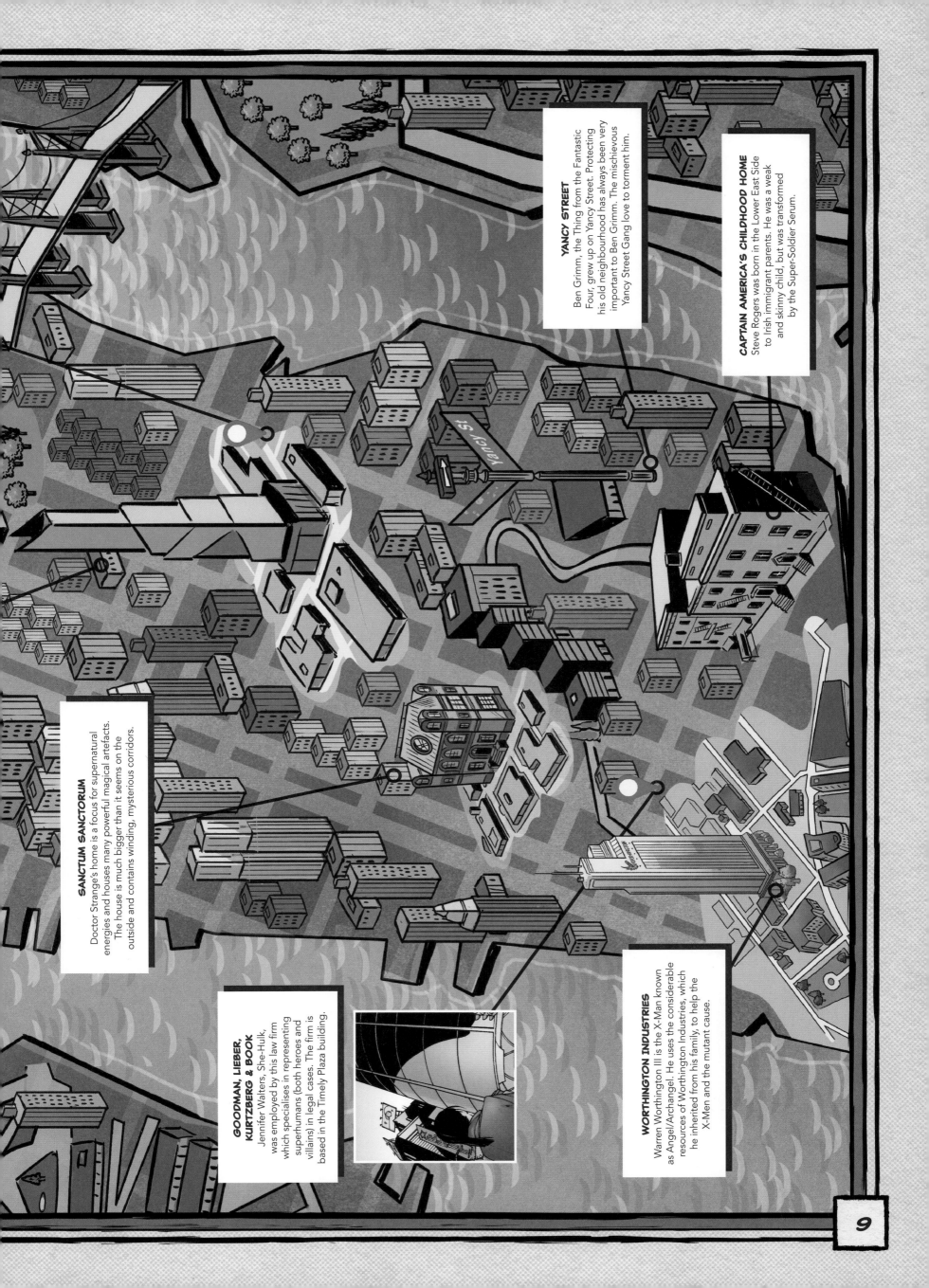

YANCY STREET

Ben Grimm, the Thing from the Fantastic Four, grew up on Yancy Street. Protecting his old neighbourhood has always been very important to Ben Grimm. The mischievous Yancy Street Gang love to torment him.

CAPTAIN AMERICA'S CHILDHOOD HOME

Steve Rogers was born in the Lower East Side to Irish immigrant parents. He was a weak and skinny child, but was transformed by the Super-Soldier Serum.

SANCTUM SANCTORUM

Doctor Strange's home is a focus for supernatural energies and houses many powerful magical artefacts. The house is much bigger than it seems on the outside and contains winding, mysterious corridors.

GOODMAN, LIEBER, KURTZBERG & BOOK

Jennifer Walters, She-Hulk, was employed by this law firm which specialises in representing superhumans (both heroes and villains) in legal cases. The firm is based in the Timely Plaza building.

WORTHINGTON INDUSTRIES

Warren Worthington III is the X-Man known as Angel/Archangel. He uses the considerable resources of Worthington Industries, which he inherited from his family, to help the X-Men and the mutant cause.

SPIDER-MAN

PETER PARKER IS NEW YORK'S RESIDENT FRIENDLY NEIGHBOURHOOD SPIDER-MAN. A BITE FROM A RADIOACTIVE SPIDER GAVE HIM INCREDIBLE POWERS, WHICH HE USES TO FIGHT CRIME AND PROTECT THE INNOCENT. SPIDER-MAN IS AN INSPIRATION TO HEROES EVERYWHERE BUT NEVER SEEMS TO BE ABLE TO CATCH A BREAK.

SPIDER-MAN'S GREATEST COSTUMES

ORIGINAL COSTUME
Peter Parker created this outfit himself, shortly after getting his powers.

BLACK COSTUME
Peter Parker returned from space with a costume that was alive! This alien costume split from Spidey and formed the antihero known as Venom.

SPIDER-ARMOUR
Sometimes, facing extra-tough bad guys requires extra-strong armour. There have been several upgrades to the Spider-Armour over the years.

IRON SPIDER
Tony Stark created this hi-tech suit full of incredible weapons and gadgets.

FUTURE FOUNDATION
Spider-Man wore this costume when he filled in for the Human Torch in the Fantastic Four.

PARKER INDUSTRIES
When Peter Parker owned his own company, he upgraded the classic Spider-Man costume.

POWERS

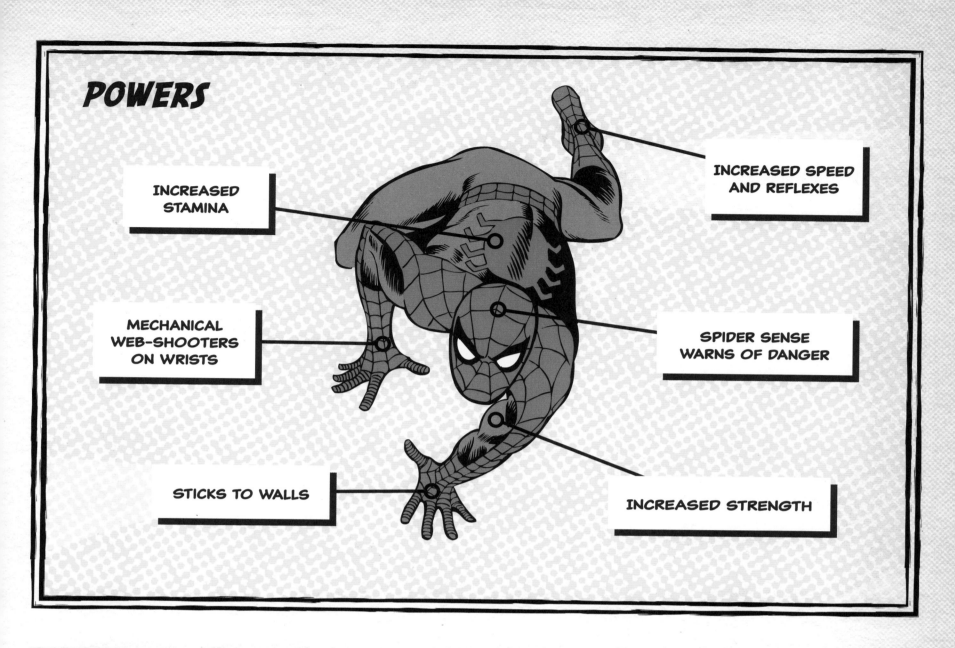

INCREASED STAMINA

INCREASED SPEED AND REFLEXES

MECHANICAL WEB-SHOOTERS ON WRISTS

SPIDER SENSE WARNS OF DANGER

STICKS TO WALLS

INCREASED STRENGTH

PETER PARKER IN NEW YORK

AUNT MAY'S HOUSE

EMPIRE STATE UNIVERSITY

PETER PARKER AND HARRY OSBORN'S APARTMENT

PETER AND MARY JANE'S APARTMENT IN CHELSEA

HOME OF THE CEO OF PARKER INDUSTRIES

BEDFORD HEIGHTS

APARTMENT IN STARK TOWERS

FLATSHARE WITH RANDY ROBERTSON AND BOOMERANG

NEW YORK: MIDTOWN, UES AND UWS

MIDTOWN, THE UPPER EAST SIDE AND THE UPPER WEST SIDE OF MANHATTAN SEEM TO BE THE CENTRE OF THE SUPER HERO UNIVERSE. DAREDEVIL PATROLS HELL'S KITCHEN, WHILE THE FANTASTIC FOUR BLAST OFF ON INCREDIBLE ADVENTURES FROM THE BAXTER BUILDING. IRON MAN AND THE AVENGERS HAVE LONG CALLED NEW YORK HOME, AND IT'S ALMOST IMPOSSIBLE NOT TO SEE SPIDER-MAN SWINGING BETWEEN SKYSCRAPERS.

LATVERIAN EMBASSY
Victor Von Doom has a base in New York, which is legally part of Latverian territory. It is manned by robots called Doombots.

NELSON AND MURDOCK LAW OFFICES
Matt Murdock and "Foggy" Nelson set up this law firm after they graduated, and they quickly employed Karen Page as a secretary. Matt and Foggy often work for free to help the people of New York.

FISK TOWER
The Kingpin looks down at the city of New York from the top of Fisk Tower. Wilson Fisk is at the centre of organised crime in New York, but likes to maintain an appearance of respectability.

HOLY GHOST CHURCH
Cloak and Dagger lived in this centrally-located abandoned church.

ALIAS INVESTIGATIONS
Jessica Jones works as a private eye, working from the Alias Investigations offices. Once a super hero herself, Jessica often works cases involving super-powers.

DAMAGE CONTROL OFFICES
This company specialises in repairing the property damage done by super hero battles.

CENTRAL PARK

SOME PRETTY INCREDIBLE THINGS HAVE HAPPENED IN THIS LARGE PARK IN THE CENTRE OF MANHATTAN.

SPIDER-MAN DEBUTS HIS BLACK COSTUME
After being taken off-planet by the Beyonder, Spider-Man and the rest of the heroes reappeared in Central Park, with Spidey sporting a brand new look.

DARK PHOENIX
The X-Men battled the Dark Phoenix here, but were no match for her powers.

PUNISHER'S FAMILY KILLED
Frank Castle's family were brutally gunned down by mobsters, sending him on his one-man war on crime.

SECRET INVASION
The final, climactic battle against the Skrull invasion of Earth took place in Central Park.

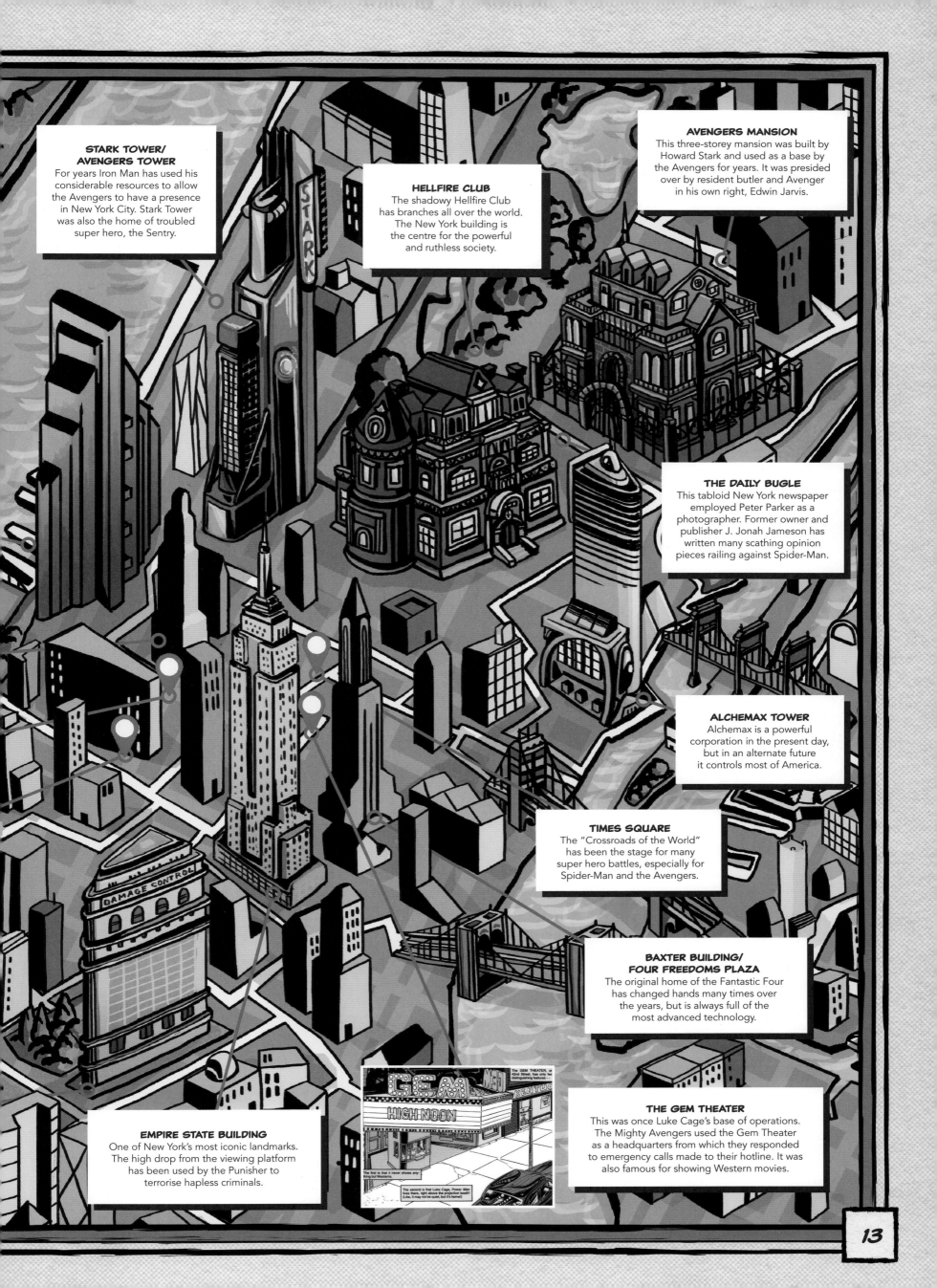

STARK TOWER/ AVENGERS TOWER
For years Iron Man has used his considerable resources to allow the Avengers to have a presence in New York City. Stark Tower was also the home of troubled super hero, the Sentry.

HELLFIRE CLUB
The shadowy Hellfire Club has branches all over the world. The New York building is the centre for the powerful and ruthless society.

AVENGERS MANSION
This three-storey mansion was built by Howard Stark and used as a base by the Avengers for years. It was presided over by resident butler and Avenger in his own right, Edwin Jarvis.

THE DAILY BUGLE
This tabloid New York newspaper employed Peter Parker as a photographer. Former owner and publisher J. Jonah Jameson has written many scathing opinion pieces railing against Spider-Man.

ALCHEMAX TOWER
Alchemax is a powerful corporation in the present day, but in an alternate future it controls most of America.

TIMES SQUARE
The "Crossroads of the World" has been the stage for many super hero battles, especially for Spider-Man and the Avengers.

BAXTER BUILDING/ FOUR FREEDOMS PLAZA
The original home of the Fantastic Four has changed hands many times over the years, but is always full of the most advanced technology.

EMPIRE STATE BUILDING
One of New York's most iconic landmarks. The high drop from the viewing platform has been used by the Punisher to terrorise hapless criminals.

THE GEM THEATER
This was once Luke Cage's base of operations. The Mighty Avengers used the Gem Theater as a headquarters from which they responded to emergency calls made to their hotline. It was also famous for showing Western movies.

FANTASTIC FOUR

THE RICHARDS FAMILY ARE ASTRONAUTS WHO WERE GIVEN THEIR POWERS WHEN THEY WERE BOMBARDED BY COSMIC RAYS. NOW THEY ARE ADVENTURERS, HEROES AND SCIENTISTS, BUT MOST IMPORTANT OF ALL, THEY ARE A FAMILY.

MR FANTASTIC
Reed Richards can stretch his body into impossible shapes and dimensions. He is the leader of the FF and one of the finest scientific minds on the planet.

HUMAN TORCH
Susan's brother Johnny can cover himself in flaming plasma and fly. Johnny is heroic but impulsive and is a "hot head" in more ways than one.

THE THING
Ben Grimm is superhumanly strong and has rock-like skin. Ben Grimm is Reed Richards' best friend, and Reed often blames himself for not being able to cure Ben's condition.

INVISIBLE WOMAN
Not only can Susan Richards turn herself and other people/things invisible, but she can create powerfully strong invisible force fields. She is married to Reed and is the lynchpin of the team.

FANTASTIC CHILDREN

FRANKLIN RICHARDS
Reed and Susan Richards' first child is a powerful mutant who has spent his entire life around super heroes.

VALERIA RICHARDS
Valeria is Franklin's younger sister, and a bona fide scientific genius in her own right. Her godfather is Victor Von Doom.

CHANGES IN THE FF LINEUP

THERE HAVE BEEN LOTS OF DIFFERENT VERSIONS OF THE TEAM AS KEY MEMBERS HAVE LEFT THE TEAM OR BEEN INCAPACITATED.

LUKE CAGE JOINS
Luke Cage filled in when Ben Grimm left the team for a while.

REED RICHARDS

SUE STORM

JOHNNY STORM

LUKE CAGE

THE NEW FANTASTIC FOUR
The Hulk, Ghost Rider, Spider-Man and Wolverine formed the new Fantastic Four when the original members were thought dead.

HULK

GHOST RIDER

SPIDER-MAN

WOLVERINE

SPIDER-MAN!
When Johnny Storm was lost in the Negative Zone, his good friend Peter Parker took his place on the team.

REED RICHARDS

SUE STORM

BEN GRIMM

SPIDER-MAN

THE FUTURE FOUNDATION
Ant-Man led Medusa, Miss Thing and She-Hulk in a temporary team while the Fantastic Four were adventuring in different time zones.

ANT-MAN

MEDUSA

MISS THING

SHE-HULK

BLACK PANTHER'S FF
Sue and Reed were briefly replaced by Black Panther and Storm.

JOHNNY STORM

BLACK PANTHER

STORM

BEN GRIMM

THE ORIGINAL BAXTER BUILDING LAYOUT

THIS 38-STOREY BUILDING IN THE HEART OF NEW YORK WAS THE HOME OF THE FANTASTIC FOUR FOR YEARS.

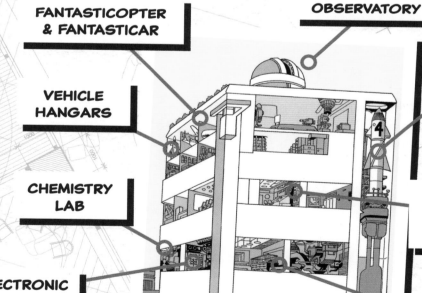

FANTASTICOPTER & FANTASTICAR

OBSERVATORY

VEHICLE HANGARS

ROCKET SILO

CHEMISTRY LAB

MISSILE MONITORING ROOM

ELECTRONIC LAB

BIOLOGICAL RESEARCH LAB

RECREATION ROOM

PRIVATE ELEVATOR

DINING ROOM

NEW YORK: UPTOWN AND HARLEM

LUKE CAGE AND THE HEROES FOR HIRE HAVE TRADITIONALLY SEEN HARLEM AS THEIR BASE OF OPERATIONS, BUT SAM WILSON (THE FALCON) HAS ALSO BEEN HARLEM'S PROTECTOR. BOTH LUKE AND SAM HAVE BEEN UNRELENTING IN THEIR WAR ON THE CRIMINAL ELEMENTS IN HARLEM, WORKING HARD TO MAKE SURE IT IS SAFE FOR THE NEXT GENERATION.

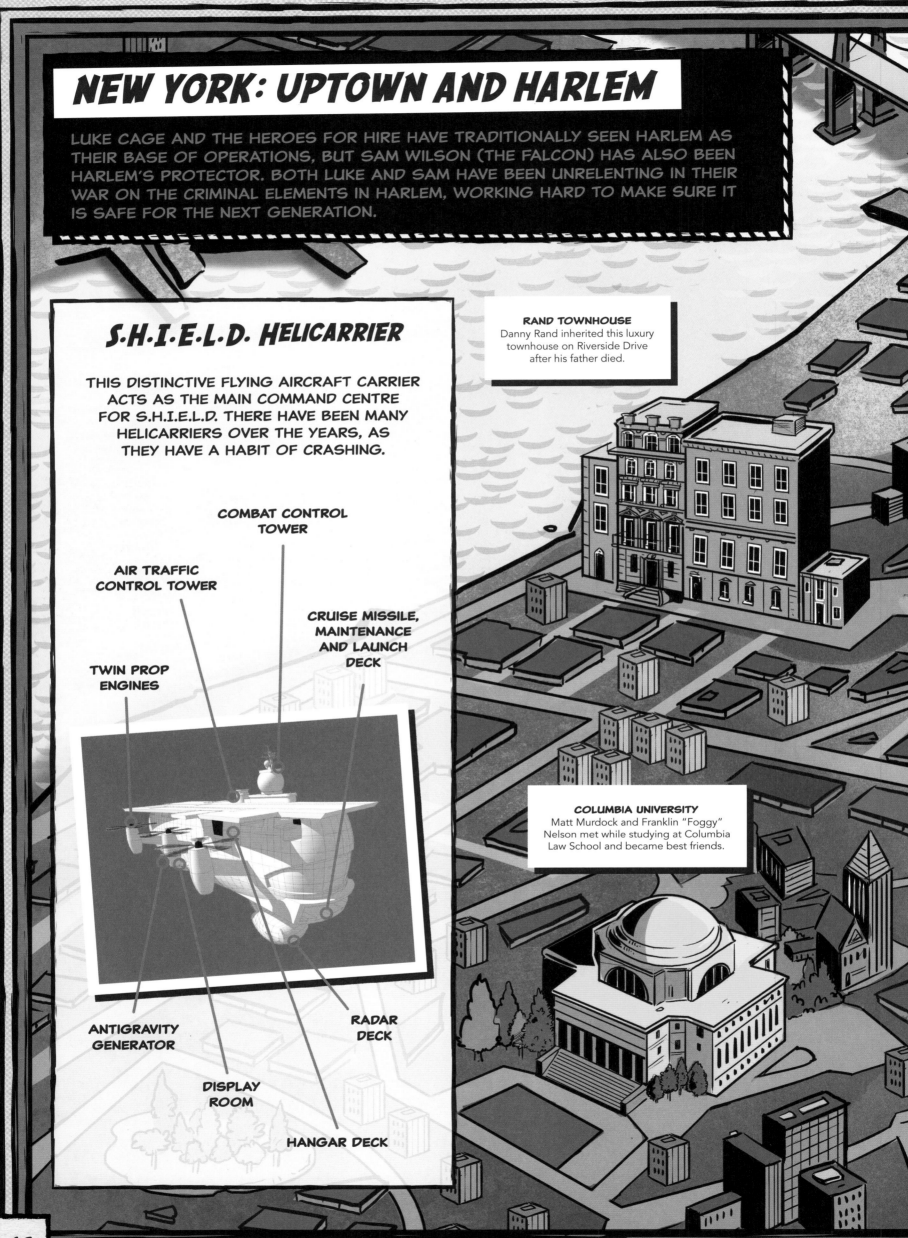

S.H.I.E.L.D. HELICARRIER

THIS DISTINCTIVE FLYING AIRCRAFT CARRIER ACTS AS THE MAIN COMMAND CENTRE FOR S.H.I.E.L.D. THERE HAVE BEEN MANY HELICARRIERS OVER THE YEARS, AS THEY HAVE A HABIT OF CRASHING.

COMBAT CONTROL TOWER

AIR TRAFFIC CONTROL TOWER

CRUISE MISSILE, MAINTENANCE AND LAUNCH DECK

TWIN PROP ENGINES

ANTIGRAVITY GENERATOR

RADAR DECK

DISPLAY ROOM

HANGAR DECK

RAND TOWNHOUSE
Danny Rand inherited this luxury townhouse on Riverside Drive after his father died.

COLUMBIA UNIVERSITY
Matt Murdock and Franklin "Foggy" Nelson met while studying at Columbia Law School and became best friends.

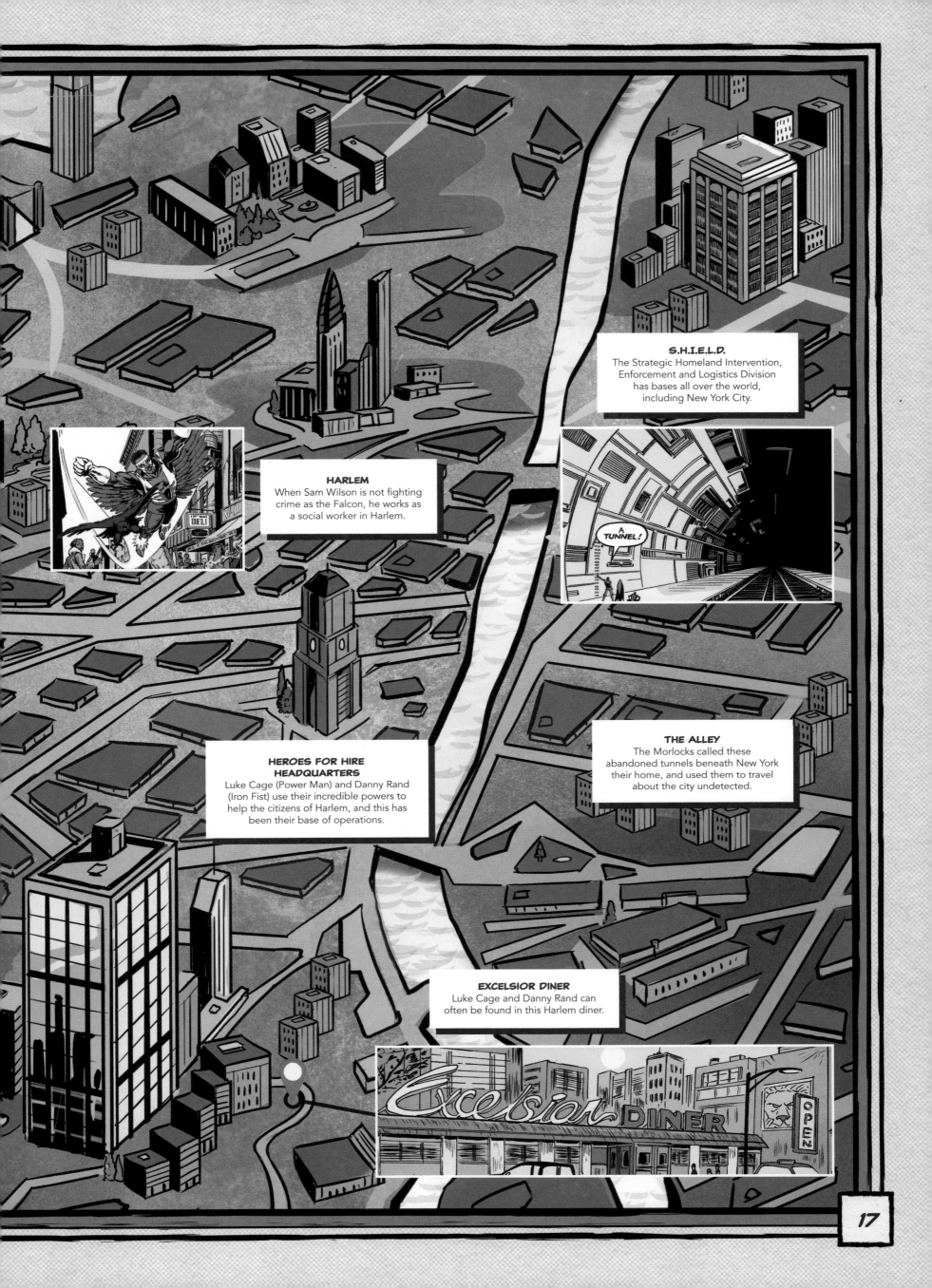

S.H.I.E.L.D.
The Strategic Homeland Intervention, Enforcement and Logistics Division has bases all over the world, including New York City.

HARLEM
When Sam Wilson is not fighting crime as the Falcon, he works as a social worker in Harlem.

A TUNNEL!

THE ALLEY
The Morlocks called these abandoned tunnels beneath New York their home, and used them to travel about the city undetected.

HEROES FOR HIRE HEADQUARTERS
Luke Cage (Power Man) and Danny Rand (Iron Fist) use their incredible powers to help the citizens of Harlem, and this has been their base of operations.

EXCELSIOR DINER
Luke Cage and Danny Rand can often be found in this Harlem diner.

NEW YORK: BEYOND MANHATTAN

NEW JERSEY, BROOKLYN, QUEENS AND UPSTATE NEW YORK ARE IMPORTANT PLACES FOR SUPER HEROES. SPIDER-MAN GREW UP AND ATTENDED SCHOOL IN QUEENS, KAMALA KHAN LIVES IN NEW JERSEY AND THE X-MEN'S XAVIER INSTITUTE IS FOUND IN UPSTATE NEW YORK. THE EAST RIVER HOLDS BOTH RYKER'S ISLAND AND THE RAFT, TWO PRISONS FOR THE DEADLIEST OF SUPER VILLAINS.

HARRY'S HIDEAWAY
A small bar which is a short walk from the Xavier Institute. The fortune of Harry's Hideaway very much depends on whether Wolverine is in town or not.

XAVIER INSTITUTE
Professor Charles Xavier turned his home into a refuge and school for mutants everywhere, teaching the dream of human and mutant co-existence.

KHAN HOUSEHOLD
Ms Marvel, Kamala Khan, lives in Jersey City with her family. She is a student at Coles Academic High School in Jersey City.

RAVENCROFT INSTITUTE FOR THE CRIMINALLY INSANE
Criminally insane villains are sent to this gothic asylum for psychiatric treatment. The Ravencroft Institute has a dark and haunted past.

PUNISHER'S HIDEOUTS
Frank Castle has secret hideouts hidden all over New York and New Jersey, all filled with weapons and ammunition.

THE STATUE OF LIBERTY
Carol Danvers, Captain Marvel, lived in the crown of the Statue of Liberty for a time.

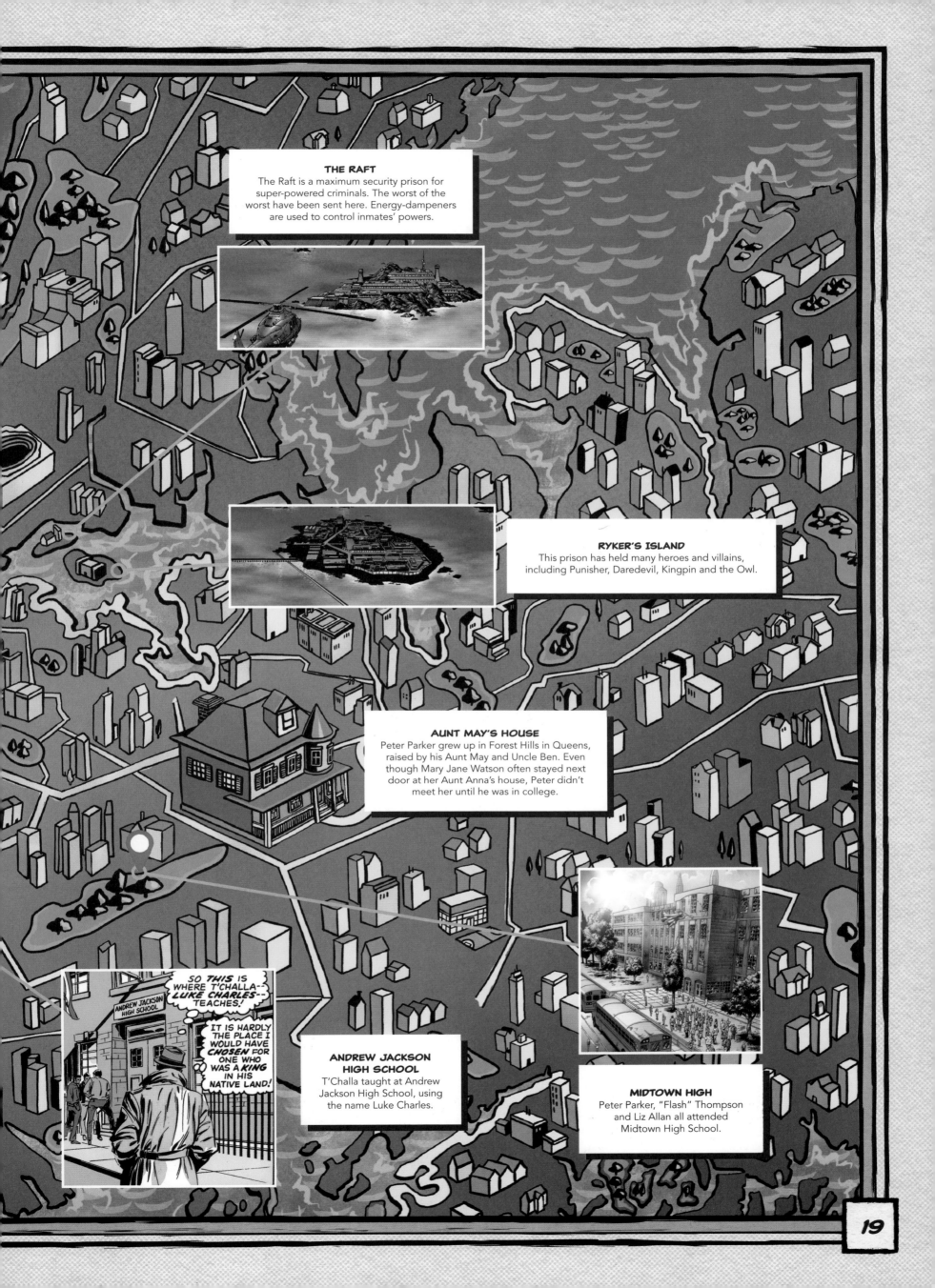

THE RAFT
The Raft is a maximum security prison for super-powered criminals. The worst of the worst have been sent here. Energy-dampeners are used to control inmates' powers.

RYKER'S ISLAND
This prison has held many heroes and villains, including Punisher, Daredevil, Kingpin and the Owl.

AUNT MAY'S HOUSE
Peter Parker grew up in Forest Hills in Queens, raised by his Aunt May and Uncle Ben. Even though Mary Jane Watson often stayed next door at her Aunt Anna's house, Peter didn't meet her until he was in college.

SO *THIS* IS WHERE T'CHALLA--*LUKE CHARLES*-- TEACHES!

IT IS HARDLY THE PLACE I WOULD HAVE *CHOSEN* FOR ONE WHO WAS A *KING* IN HIS NATIVE LAND!

ANDREW JACKSON HIGH SCHOOL

ANDREW JACKSON HIGH SCHOOL
T'Challa taught at Andrew Jackson High School, using the name Luke Charles.

MIDTOWN HIGH
Peter Parker, "Flash" Thompson and Liz Allan all attended Midtown High School.

THE X-MEN

THE X-MEN ARE MUTANT HEROES WHO HAVE COME TOGETHER AS PART OF PROFESSOR XAVIER'S DREAM OF PEACE BETWEEN HUMANS AND MUTANTS.

PROFESSOR X
CHARLES XAVIER
Telepathy

CYCLOPS
SCOTT SUMMERS
Optic blasts

ICEMAN
ROBERT "BOBBY" DRAKE
Temperature manipulation

BEAST
HANK MCCOY
Genius/Enhanced physical abilities

ANGEL
WARREN WORTHINGTON III
Flight

JEAN GREY
Telekinesis, telepathy

LATER RECRUITS

NIGHTCRAWLER
KURT WAGNER
Teleportation

WOLVERINE
JAMES "LOGAN" HOWLETT
Adamantium-plated bones and claws/ healing factor/heightened senses

BANSHEE
SEAN CASSIDY
Enhanced vocal cords

STORM
ORORO MUNROE
Weather control

SUNFIRE
SHIRO YOSHIDA
Flight, plasma blasts

COLOSSUS
PIOTR RASPUTIN
Organic steel-like skin

SHADOWCAT
KATE "KITTY" PRYDE
Intangibility

ROGUE
ANNE MARIE
Super strength/ power absorption

RACHEL SUMMERS
Telepathy, telekinesis

PSYLOCKE
BETSY BRADDOCK
Telekinetic weapons

DAZZLER
ALISON BLAIRE
Converts sound into light

GAMBIT
REMY LEBEAU
Charges objects with kinetic energy

JUBILEE
JUBILATION LEE
Pyrokinetic energy blasts

BISHOP
LUCAS BISHOP
Energy absorption/ projection, detective

CABLE
NATHAN SUMMERS
Psychic, time-travelling soldier

WHITE QUEEN
EMMA FROST
Telepathy, diamond hard form

MAGIK
ILLYANA RAPUTINA
Teleportation, sorceress

NEW MUTANTS

MIRAGE
DANIELLE MOONSTONE
Psychic arrow projection

CANNONBALL
SAM GUTHRIE
Jet propulsion

CHAMBER
JONOTHON STARSMORE
Telepathy, psionic furnace in chest

WOLFSBANE
RAHNE SINCLAIR
Lycanthropy

SUNSPOT
ROBERTO "BOBBY" DA COSTA
Solar energy manipulation and redirection

X-FORCE (OVER THE YEARS)

CABLE
NATHAN SUMMERS
Telekinesis, telepathy

BISHOP
LUCAS BISHOP
Energy absorption and redirection

PSYLOCKE
BETSY BRADDOCK
Telekinetic weapons

WARPATH
JAMES PROUDSTAR
Superhuman strength, agility, stamina

DOMINO
NEENA THURMAN
Luck manipulation

X-FACTOR (OVER THE YEARS)

HAVOK
ALEX SUMMERS
Energy blasts

POLARIS
LORNA DANE
Manipulation of magnetic fields

LONGSHOT
Acrobat, luck manipulation

MULTIPLE MAN
JAMIE MADROX
Creates duplicates of self

NORTHSTAR
JEAN-PAUL BEAUBIER
Flight, superhuman speed

XAVIER INSTITUTE

THE X-MANSION IS THE ANCESTRAL HOME OF CHARLES XAVIER, WHICH BECAME A SCHOOL AND HAVEN FOR MUTANTS EVERYWHERE. JUST LIKE ITS INHABITANTS, IT HAS MUTATED INTO DIFFERENT FORMS OVER THE YEARS AND HAS BEEN KNOWN AS THE XAVIER INSTITUTE FOR GIFTED YOUNGSTERS, THE JEAN GREY SCHOOL FOR HIGHER LEARNING, X-HAVEN AND THE XAVIER INSTITUTE FOR MUTANT EDUCATION AND OUTREACH.

DANGER ROOM
For years X-Men trained in the Danger Room, which honed their abilities using state of the art effects. The Danger Room became sentient and called itself Danger, first fighting then joining the X-Men.

BASKETBALL COURT
The X-Mansion basketball court covers the Blackbird jet plane hangar underneath.

CEREBRO
This incredible device enhances psychic abilities and was created by Professor X. It once took up a whole room of the Xavier Institute, but Professor X now uses a portable version.

EAST USA

FROM THE MAN-THING'S SUPERNATURAL SWAMP IN FLORIDA TO THE HERO TRAINING GROUNDS IN CAMP HAMMOND IN CONNECTICUT, THERE IS A HUGE AMOUNT OF RAW SUPER-POWER ON THE EASTERN SEABOARD. RAW POLITICAL POWER FLOWS FROM WASHINGTON DC, WHICH HAS NEVER BEEN TOO TRUSTING OF SUPER HEROES.

DETROIT – FOUNDING PLACE OF THE AVENGERS
The Avengers' first team-up took place in an auto factory in Detroit, where Thor, Hulk, Iron Man, Ant-Man and the Wasp teamed up to fight Loki.

THE BAR WITH NO NAME
There are many Bars With No Name which are hangouts for super criminals. The Bar With No Name in Medina County, Ohio, was where Scourge killed many super criminals.

WASHINGTON DC'S GREATEST BATTLES

THE CAPITAL OF THE UNITED STATES OF AMERICA HAS SEEN SOME SIGNIFICANT SUPER-POWERED BATTLES.

AVENGERS VS KANG
During the time-travelling Kang's subjugation of Earth, the Avengers battled his forces in DC and around the world.

IRON MAN VS TITANIUM MAN
Tony Stark and Boris Bullski fought in the skies high above Washington DC when Iron Man was on his way to testify before Congress.

AVENGERS VS ULTIMO
The Mandarin sent Ultimo to attack Washington DC, but the Avengers beat him back and threw him into a volcano.

CAPTAIN AMERICA VS CAPTAIN AMERICA
During the Hydra takeover of America, Steve Rogers fought an evil, Hydra-obsessed version of himself created by the Cosmic Cube.

SEAGATE PRISON
Luke Cage was imprisoned in Seagate Prison, where he was subjected to experimental treatments which gave him his incredible powers. Seagate is sometimes known as "Little Alcatraz".

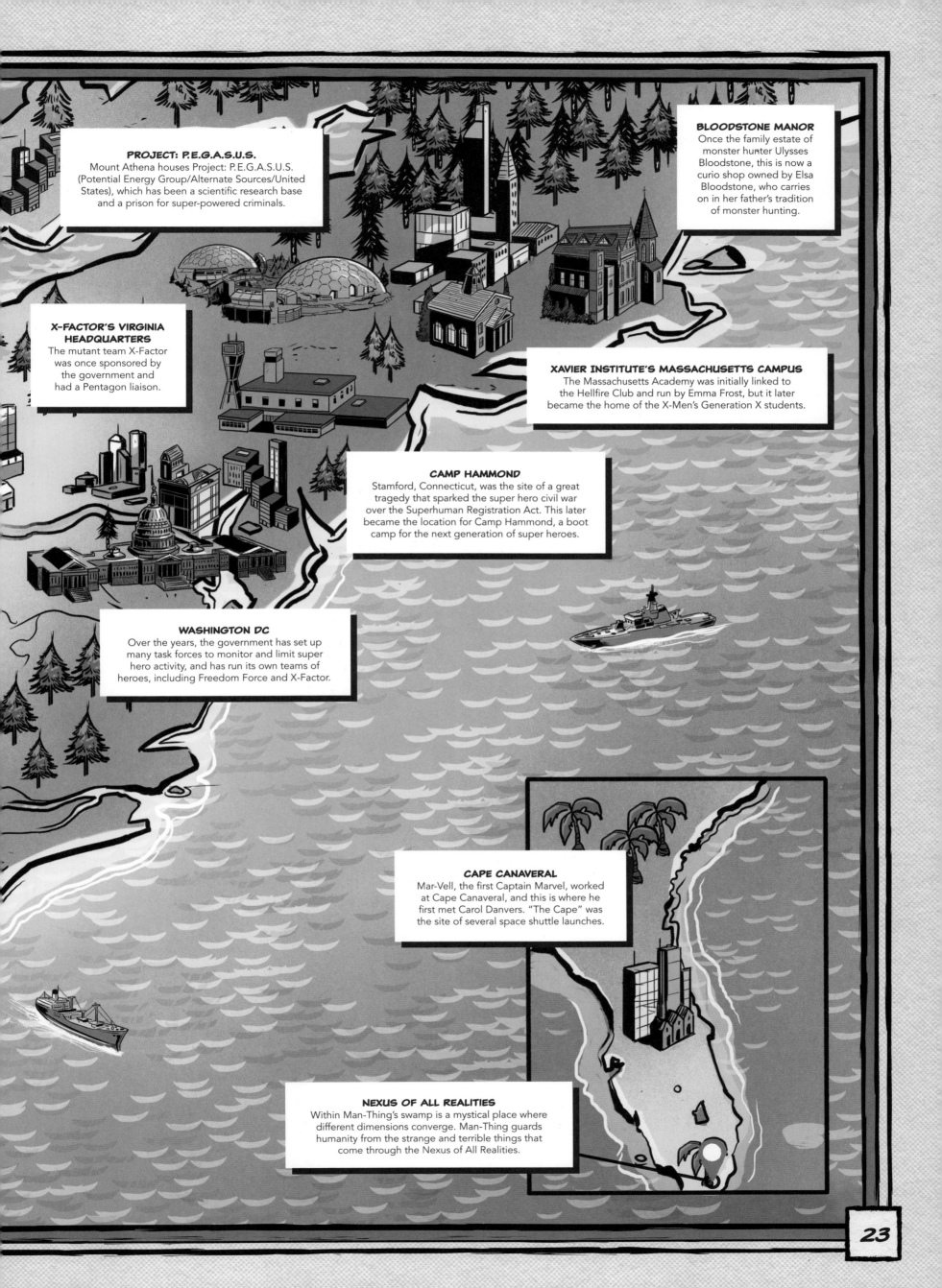

PROJECT: P.E.G.A.S.U.S.
Mount Athena houses Project: P.E.G.A.S.U.S. (Potential Energy Group/Alternate Sources/United States), which has been a scientific research base and a prison for super-powered criminals.

BLOODSTONE MANOR
Once the family estate of monster hunter Ulysses Bloodstone, this is now a curio shop owned by Elsa Bloodstone, who carries on in her father's tradition of monster hunting.

X-FACTOR'S VIRGINIA HEADQUARTERS
The mutant team X-Factor was once sponsored by the government and had a Pentagon liaison.

XAVIER INSTITUTE'S MASSACHUSETTS CAMPUS
The Massachusetts Academy was initially linked to the Hellfire Club and run by Emma Frost, but it later became the home of the X-Men's Generation X students.

CAMP HAMMOND
Stamford, Connecticut, was the site of a great tragedy that sparked the super hero civil war over the Superhuman Registration Act. This later became the location for Camp Hammond, a boot camp for the next generation of super heroes.

WASHINGTON DC
Over the years, the government has set up many task forces to monitor and limit super hero activity, and has run its own teams of heroes, including Freedom Force and X-Factor.

CAPE CANAVERAL
Mar-Vell, the first Captain Marvel, worked at Cape Canaveral, and this is where he first met Carol Danvers. "The Cape" was the site of several space shuttle launches.

NEXUS OF ALL REALITIES
Within Man-Thing's swamp is a mystical place where different dimensions converge. Man-Thing guards humanity from the strange and terrible things that come through the Nexus of All Realities.

CAPTAIN AMERICA

STEVE ROGERS IS THE SUPER HERO'S SUPER HERO. THE SENTINEL OF LIBERTY IS A LIVING LEGEND WHO IS THE NATURAL LEADER OF THE AVENGERS. THE SUPER-SOLDIER SERUM MADE HIM A SPECIMEN OF PHYSICAL FITNESS, BUT STEVE ROGERS' REAL STRENGTH IS THAT HE HAS THE INDOMITABLE SPIRIT OF A HERO.

POWERS

SUPERB MILITARY TACTICIAN

WOVEN CHAIN ARMOUR UNIFORM

MASTER HAND-TO-HAND COMBATANT

VIBRANIUM-ADAMANTIUM ALLOY SHIELD

ENHANCED DURABILITY

CAPTAIN AMERICA'S HISTORY

SUPER-SOLDIER SERUM

Steve Rogers was not physically fit enough to sign up to fight in World War II, so he volunteered to take the experimental Super-Soldier Serum. Transformed into the ultimate soldier, he fought bravely for the Allies.

LOST IN THE ICE

At the end of the war, Captain America went missing during a fight with Baron Zemo and was frozen solid in the ocean. He was found by Namor decades later and revived by the Avengers.

REVIVED

A man out of time, Steve Rogers found it hard to adjust to the modern day. Times have changed, and the world that he remembers has long gone.

THE AVENGERS

Captain America has been the leader of countless teams of Avengers, inspiring heroes around him to save the day.

THE RED SKULL

One constant in Captain America's life has been his nemesis, the Red Skull. From World War II to the present day, Johann Schmidt has been Steve Rogers' archenemy.

OTHER CAPTAIN AMERICAS

THE LEGEND OF CAPTAIN AMERICA IS TOO BIG FOR JUST ONE MAN, SO WHEN STEVE ROGERS HAS BEEN UNABLE TO LIFT THE SHIELD OTHER HEROES HAVE STEPPED IN TO FILL THE ROLE OF CAP.

U.S.AGENT

John Walker was originally called the Super Patriot, but he took the role of Captain America when Steve Rogers was forced to resign for a time. When Steve returned, John Walker became the U.S.Agent.

BUCKY BARNES

James Buchanan "Bucky" Barnes became Captain America after he shook the mental conditioning that turned him into the Winter Soldier.

SAM WILSON

Sam has been Steve's ally as the Falcon for years, but he has also stepped in to wield the shield when needed. Even when he was Captain America, Sam still kept his signature wings.

SAN FRANCISCO

SAN FRANCISCO HAS ALWAYS BEEN A FRIENDLY AND WELCOMING PLACE FOR SUPER HEROES. DAREDEVIL, BLACK WIDOW AND THE X-MEN HAVE ALL LIVED IN SAN FRANCISCO AT ONE TIME OR ANOTHER. SAN FRANCISCO BAY SEEMS TO BE A MAGNET FOR MONSTER AND ALIEN INVASIONS, BUT THANKFULLY THERE ARE ALWAYS HEROES ON HAND TO SAVE THE DAY.

GOLDEN GATE BRIDGE
The Hulk and Red Hulk fought on the Golden Gate Bridge in a battle that was so intense that it almost destroyed the bridge itself.

GRAYMALKIN INDUSTRIES
The X-Men used this as their base in San Francisco before they moved to the island of Utopia.

GOLDEN GATE PARK
Golden Gate Park was home to the Dreaming Celestial for a time, a massively powerful cosmic being.

BLACK WIDOW'S MANSION
Black Widow and Daredevil lived together for a while in San Francisco when they were a couple.

HORIZON UNIVERSITY
A disguised Otto Octavius worked in this institute for higher education. It is staffed by ex-Parker Industries employees.

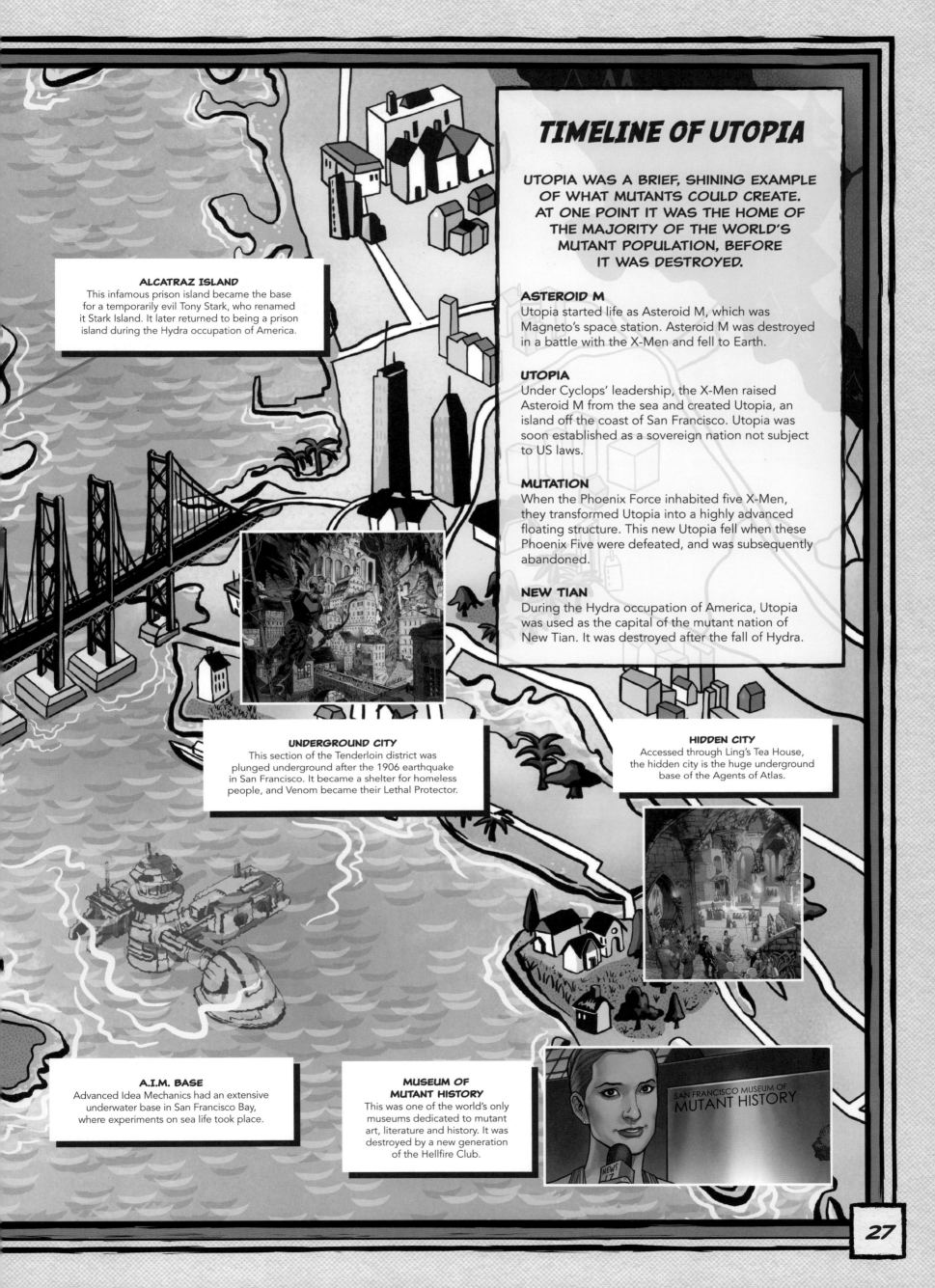

ALCATRAZ ISLAND
This infamous prison island became the base for a temporarily evil Tony Stark, who renamed it Stark Island. It later returned to being a prison island during the Hydra occupation of America.

TIMELINE OF UTOPIA

UTOPIA WAS A BRIEF, SHINING EXAMPLE OF WHAT MUTANTS *COULD* CREATE. AT ONE POINT IT WAS THE HOME OF THE MAJORITY OF THE WORLD'S MUTANT POPULATION, BEFORE IT WAS DESTROYED.

ASTEROID M
Utopia started life as Asteroid M, which was Magneto's space station. Asteroid M was destroyed in a battle with the X-Men and fell to Earth.

UTOPIA
Under Cyclops' leadership, the X-Men raised Asteroid M from the sea and created Utopia, an island off the coast of San Francisco. Utopia was soon established as a sovereign nation not subject to US laws.

MUTATION
When the Phoenix Force inhabited five X-Men, they transformed Utopia into a highly advanced floating structure. This new Utopia fell when these Phoenix Five were defeated, and was subsequently abandoned.

NEW TIAN
During the Hydra occupation of America, Utopia was used as the capital of the mutant nation of New Tian. It was destroyed after the fall of Hydra.

UNDERGROUND CITY
This section of the Tenderloin district was plunged underground after the 1906 earthquake in San Francisco. It became a shelter for homeless people, and Venom became their Lethal Protector.

HIDDEN CITY
Accessed through Ling's Tea House, the hidden city is the huge underground base of the Agents of Atlas.

A.I.M. BASE
Advanced Idea Mechanics had an extensive underwater base in San Francisco Bay, where experiments on sea life took place.

MUSEUM OF MUTANT HISTORY
This was one of the world's only museums dedicated to mutant art, literature and history. It was destroyed by a new generation of the Hellfire Club.

LOS ANGELES

THERE AREN'T MANY CITIES THAT HAVE THEIR OWN AVENGERS TEAM, BUT LA IS NEVER A CITY TO FALL BEHIND NEW YORK, SO THE CITY OF ANGELS HAS THE WEST COAST AVENGERS. TONY STARK IS ALSO A BIG FAN OF THE GLAMOUR OF LA AND HAS A HOUSE BUILT INTO THE CLIFFS IN MALIBU.

THE RETREAT
Tony Stark had a state-of-the-art mansion built into the cliffs in Malibu, and it housed many of his suits of Iron Man armour.

STARK ENTERPRISES TOWER
Tony Stark has buildings all over the world. Stark Enterprises Tower was one of the corporation's public headquarters.

WHO IS GHOST RIDER?

THE CURSE OF GHOST RIDER HAS BEEN PASSED BETWEEN DIFFERENT HEROES. DIFFERENT GHOST RIDERS HAVE DIFFERENT POWERS AND HISTORIES, BUT ALL ARE DRIVEN BY A THIRST FOR VENGEANCE.

JOHNNY BLAZE
Stunt rider Johnny Blaze traded his soul to Mephisto and was bonded with the demon Zarathos. At night he became the flame-skulled Ghost Rider.

DANNY KETCH
When Danny Ketch touched a mystical motorcycle fuel cap he became the Spirit of Vengeance. Danny later discovered he was Johnny Blaze's long-lost half-brother.

ROBBIE REYES
Unlike his predecessors, Robbie Reyes favours a car. He rides a flaming car known as the Hellcharger instead of a motorbike.

COSMIC GHOST RIDER
An alternate future version of Frank Castle made a deal with Mephisto, then a deal with Galactus, then a deal with Thanos. His mind broken, he became Cosmic Ghost Rider.

HAWKEYE INVESTIGATIONS
Kate Bishop lives and works as Hawkeye Investigations, despite not having an official private investigator's license. Her office later became the home of the new West Coast Avengers.

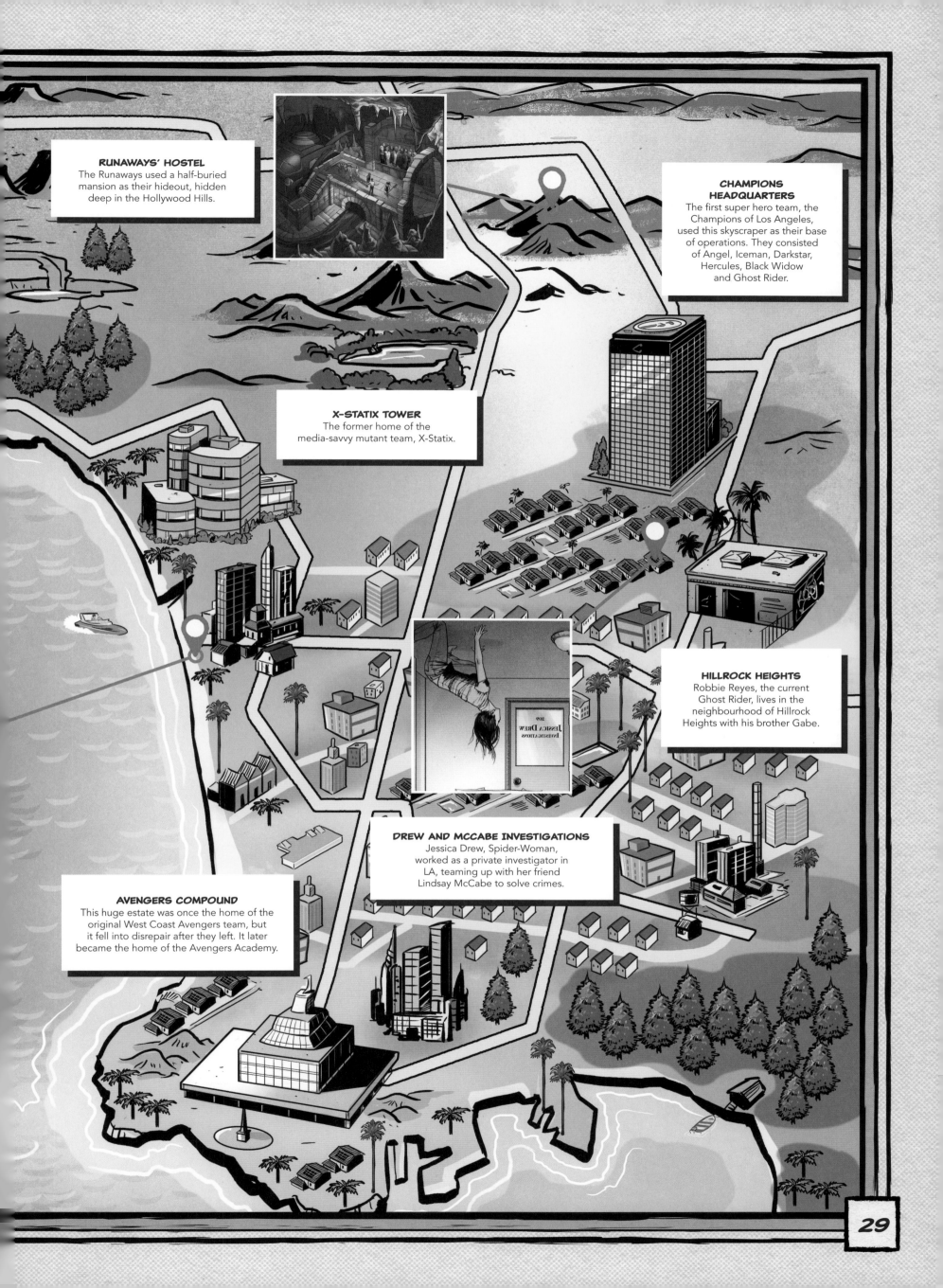

RUNAWAYS' HOSTEL
The Runaways used a half-buried mansion as their hideout, hidden deep in the Hollywood Hills.

CHAMPIONS HEADQUARTERS
The first super hero team, the Champions of Los Angeles, used this skyscraper as their base of operations. They consisted of Angel, Iceman, Darkstar, Hercules, Black Widow and Ghost Rider.

X-STATIX TOWER
The former home of the media-savvy mutant team, X-Statix.

HILLROCK HEIGHTS
Robbie Reyes, the current Ghost Rider, lives in the neighbourhood of Hillrock Heights with his brother Gabe.

DREW AND McCABE INVESTIGATIONS
Jessica Drew, Spider-Woman, worked as a private investigator in LA, teaming up with her friend Lindsay McCabe to solve crimes.

AVENGERS COMPOUND
This huge estate was once the home of the original West Coast Avengers team, but it fell into disrepair after they left. It later became the home of the Avengers Academy.

IRON MAN

AFTER BEING WOUNDED AND KIDNAPPED, TONY STARK CREATED A SUIT OF ARMOUR TO HELP HIM ESCAPE HIS CAPTORS. NOW HE PROTECTS THE WORLD AS IRON MAN, A SUPER HERO AND ONE OF THE ORIGINAL MEMBERS OF THE AVENGERS. TONY STARK IS A TECHNOLOGICAL GENIUS AND IS ALWAYS UPGRADING HIS IRON MAN ARMOUR AND GADGETS.

GREATEST IRON MAN SUITS

ORIGINAL ARMOUR
This was the armour that started Tony on the road to becoming a super hero. It was built from scraps of machinery while Tony was held in captivity. Once Tony escaped he upgraded the armour, adding jet boots and painting it gold.

RED AND GOLD ARMOUR
The classic Iron Man look was an upgrade from his original suit. Not only was it stronger and faster than his original suit, but it could be stored in a suitcase and brought out in emergencies.

STEALTH SUIT
Iron Man may look impressive, but he is not exactly inconspicuous. Tony built the Stealth Suit for missions that require a lighter touch. It is undetectable by radar and has technology that makes it invisible to the human eye.

SILVER CENTURION
This silver and red look was bulkier and more powerful than the standard Iron Man armour.

HULKBUSTER ARMOUR
Tony Stark plans for every eventuality, and the super-strong Hulkbuster armour was created to deal with Hulk-level threats.

NANOTECH SUIT
Stark created an armour using advanced nanotech that allows him to change the armour into any configuration or visual and assume the property of any of his previous armours.

WAR MACHINE
The weapon-studded War Machine armour was built for Tony Stark, but now belongs to Tony's best friend James "Rhodey" Rhodes, who has become a hero.

IRON SPIDER
Stark created a suit of armour perfect for Spider-Man, one complete with four retractable spider legs, giving Spidey an even more spidery appearance.

RESCUE
Tony Stark created this suit of armour for Pepper Potts, and she has used it to continue Iron Man's legacy when he has been out of action.

STARK INDUSTRIES

CREATED BY TONY STARK'S GREAT GRANDFATHER, DR ISAAC STARK SR, STARK INDUSTRIES HAS BEEN A GLOBAL INDUSTRIAL SUPERPOWER FOR OVER A CENTURY. UNDER TONY STARK, THE COMPANY BECAME SYNONYMOUS WITH INNOVATION. STARK INDUSTRIES WAS ABLE TO DEVELOP AND MANUFACTURE SOME OF THE MOST ADVANCED TECHNOLOGY IN THE WORLD.

STARK TOWER
Located in Manhattan, Stark Tower has served as Tony Stark's home as well as being a hotbed for design and innovation. Tony allowed the Avengers to use it as a base, but it was still the headquarters of Stark Industries.

STARK SOLUTIONS
During the period that Stark Enterprises was controlled by Fujikawa Industries, Tony Stark launched Stark Solutions, which soon became a formidable company in itself.

STARK UNLIMITED
Tony eventually brought all the Stark companies back under the Stark Unlimited conglomerate. Stark Unlimited was meant to be the next wave of innovation and a test bed for new technologies. The company was later taken over by Tony's adoptive brother Arno Stark.

STARK RESILIENT
Stark Resilient used Tony Stark's repulsor technology to create vehicles and civilian technology. This repulsor tech was used to create Asgardia, the floating City of Asgard.

STARK-FUJIKAWA
When Tony Stark was thought dead, his company was bought by the Fujikawa Family, who maintained control of the company for some time.

WEST USA

THE WEST COAST OF AMERICA HAS OFTEN BEEN THE STOMPING GROUND FOR THE INCREDIBLE HULK. BORN IN THE HEAT OF THE NEW MEXICO DESERT, THE HULK HAS ALSO FOUND A HOME IN LAS VEGAS AT TIMES. THE RELATIVELY UNASSUMING BROXTON, OKLAHOMA, WAS A TEMPORARY SITE FOR ASGARD, WHICH PROVED QUITE A CULTURE SHOCK FOR THE GODS AND THEIR HOSTS.

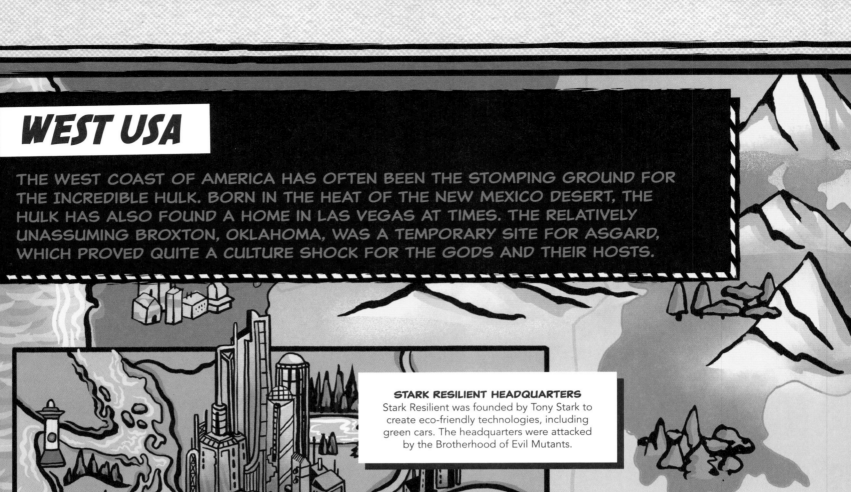

STARK RESILIENT HEADQUARTERS
Stark Resilient was founded by Tony Stark to create eco-friendly technologies, including green cars. The headquarters were attacked by the Brotherhood of Evil Mutants.

HOTEL INFERNO
The demon Mephisto created the Hotel Inferno in Las Vegas. Doctor Strange used magic to trap Mephisto in the top floor of the hotel.

DUNWICH SANITORIUM
Wolverine was a patient of the insane Doctor Rot at the Dunwich Sanitorium. Logan escaped, but with psychological scars.

THE MOUNT
This was the base of the Pantheon, a super powered group who were descended from a half-Asgardian called Agamemnon. For a while, the Hulk was allied with this group.

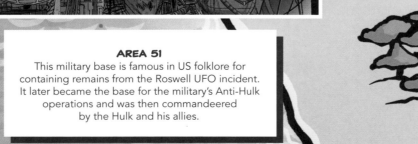

AREA 51
This military base is famous in US folklore for containing remains from the Roswell UFO incident. It later became the base for the military's Anti-Hulk operations and was then commandeered by the Hulk and his allies.

LAS VEGAS
Joe Fixit, one of the Hulk's personalities, spent time working as a mob enforcer in Vegas.

QUENTIN CARNIVAL ROUTE
Ghost Rider Johnny Blaze was a motorcycle stunt rider in the Quentin Carnival, a travelling festival owned and operated by Ralph Quentin.

THE VAULT
The Vault was a maximum security prison for super villains. Its inmates were so dangerous that it initially contained a bomb that would detonate in the event of a breakout. After the bomb was deactivated, the Vault suffered a series of riots and escapes and was eventually closed.

THUNDERBOLTS MOUNTAIN
The superhumans known as the Thunderbolts used this as their base. It later became the headquarters for Norman Osborn's H.A.M.M.E.R. organisation.

LOS DIABLOS DESERT BASE
This is the site of the Gamma Bomb test that turned Bruce Banner into the Hulk. The Hulk can always find his way back here, no matter where he is on Earth.

THE THUNDERBOLTS

CAN VILLAINS EVER TRULY REFORM, AND SHOULD THEY BE ALLOWED TO? THE THUNDERBOLTS HAVE ALWAYS BEEN MADE UP OF DARK AND UNTRUSTWORTHY FIGURES, BUT SOMETIMES THEY DO THE RIGHT THING.

THE MASTERS OF EVIL
The first incarnation of the Thunderbolts was created by Baron Zemo from many former members of the Masters of Evil. Presenting themselves as super heroes, they tried to get power and authority, but eventually enjoyed being the good guys.

HAWKEYE'S THUNDERBOLTS
Hawkeye, a former villain himself, led the team for a while. He tried to find pardons for the criminal members of the team.

NORMAN OSBORN'S THUNDERBOLTS
Spider-Man's nemesis, Norman Osborn (the Green Goblin), acted as the director of a Thunderbolts team for a while, one that included the incredibly violent Bullseye and Venom, and carried out dangerous black ops missions.

LUKE CAGE'S THUNDERBOLTS
After Norman Osborn fell, Luke Cage took on leadership of the team as a favour to Steve Rogers. Several misunderstood heroes, like Man-Thing, were part of his team.

WINTER SOLDIER'S THUNDERBOLTS
The Winter Soldier reassembled members of the original Thunderbolts to help him fight interplanetary threats, but had power wrestled away from him by Baron Zemo.

BROXTON, OKLAHOMA
After a Ragnarok cycle, Thor recreated Asgard as a floating city a few miles outside Broxton, Oklahoma, paying for the land with Asgardian treasure. It was eventually replaced with the moving city of Asgardia.

THE HULK

CAUGHT IN THE INCREDIBLE FORCE OF AN EXPERIMENTAL GAMMA BOMB, DOCTOR BRUCE BANNER WAS TRANSFORMED INTO A CREATURE OF ALMOST LIMITLESS RAGE AND POWER. ALTHOUGH HE IS A HERO AND A FOUNDING MEMBER OF THE AVENGERS, THE HULK HAS STRUGGLED TO FIND PEACE AND ACCEPTANCE IN THE WORLD.

DIFFERENT INCARNATIONS OF THE HULK

THE LOOK, INTELLIGENCE AND PHYSICAL POWER OF THE HULK CAN CHANGE DEPENDING ON THE LEVELS OF GAMMA RADIATION IN BRUCE BANNER, AND ON HIS OWN MENTAL STATE.

BRUCE BANNER
A reserved and thoughtful scientist, Doctor Robert Bruce Banner is a genius-level inventor.

THE INCREDIBLE HULK
The Hulk shares his body with Banner, at first coming out only at night, then when Banner was angry. The angrier Hulk gets, the stronger Hulk gets, and the upper limits of his strength may not yet have been measured.

JOE FIXIT
This aspect of the Hulk is a Vegas enforcer called Joe Fixit. Joe has grey skin and while he is not quite as strong as the green Hulk, he is smarter and has a much wider vocabulary.

THE PROFESSOR
Banner, Fixit and the savage Hulk merged to create a Hulk who was smart, confident and incredibly strong.

GREEN SCAR
When the Hulk was a gladiator on the savage planet of Sakaar he was known as the Green Scar because of a wound he sustained in the arena.

THE IMMORTAL HULK
Though Bruce Banner arranged for his own assassination to stop the Hulk's threat to Earth, he soon learned that the Hulk could overcome death itself. The Immortal Hulk is darker than the other incarnations of the Hulk.

MAESTRO
This evil alternate future version of the Hulk rules a society called Dystopia with violence and cruelty. The idea that he might become the Maestro haunts the Hulk.

OTHER HULKS

THE HULK'S IMMENSE POWER HAS NOT JUST BEEN KEPT TO BRUCE BANNER.

SHE-HULK
Jennifer Walters is Bruce Banner's cousin. When Jennifer needed an emergency blood transfusion Bruce was the only match, which turned her into a female version of the Hulk. Jennifer has human and Hulk forms, but is a smart, competent lawyer in both.

RED HULK
General Thaddeus "Thunderbolt" Ross spent years chasing the Hulk and eventually submitted himself to gamma radiation which turned him into the Hulk's enemy, Red Hulk.

RED SHE-HULK
Betty Ross, Bruce Banner's ex-wife and Thunderbolt Ross's daughter, was given incredible power as the Red She-Hulk.

BRAWN
Genius Amadeus Cho was a friend of the Hulk who was given Hulk's power after removing it from Banner using nanites. Banner later regained his powers, and Cho embarked on his own super hero adventures.

CANADA

THE OFFICIAL CANADIAN SUPER HERO TEAM IS ALPHA FLIGHT, CREATED BY JAMES MACDONALD HUDSON AND THE CANADIAN GOVERNMENT'S DEPARTMENT H. CANADA WAS NOT ONLY WOLVERINE'S BIRTHPLACE, BUT WAS ALSO WHERE HE WAS GIVEN HIS ADAMANTIUM BONES AND CLAWS.

THE ICE BOX
Canada's superhuman maximum security prison is located deep in the inhospitable Northwest Territories and has many fewer escape attempts than American jails.

MAISON ALPHA
Alpha Flight used this building as their base, which they believed was built on a dimensional well of mystic energy.

WEAPON X FACILITY
This shadowy government facility is where Wolverine was given his Adamantium bones and claws. Years later, Cyclops used it as a base for his team of outlaw X-Men.

HOWLETT ESTATE
James Howlett, the man who would become Wolverine, grew up in the 1890s in Alberta, Canada. He fled the family home not long after first exhibiting his mutant powers.

MANSION ALPHA
Mansion Alpha was on Tamarind Island, which was owned by Walter Langkowski, aka Sasquatch. The mansion was Alpha Flight's headquarters until it was destroyed by the villain Bedlam.

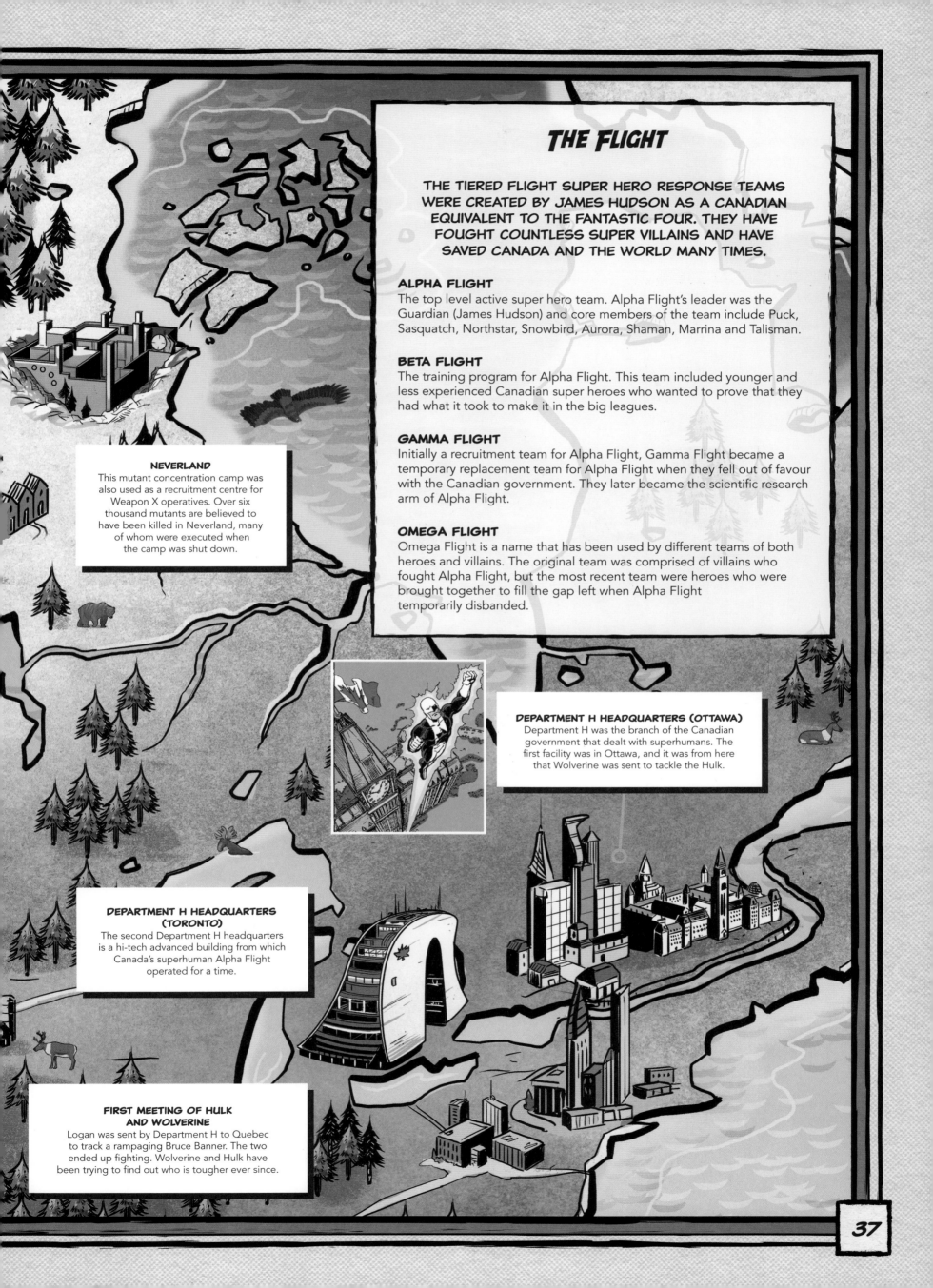

THE FLIGHT

THE TIERED FLIGHT SUPER HERO RESPONSE TEAMS WERE CREATED BY JAMES HUDSON AS A CANADIAN EQUIVALENT TO THE FANTASTIC FOUR. THEY HAVE FOUGHT COUNTLESS SUPER VILLAINS AND HAVE SAVED CANADA AND THE WORLD MANY TIMES.

ALPHA FLIGHT
The top level active super hero team. Alpha Flight's leader was the Guardian (James Hudson) and core members of the team include Puck, Sasquatch, Northstar, Snowbird, Aurora, Shaman, Marrina and Talisman.

BETA FLIGHT
The training program for Alpha Flight. This team included younger and less experienced Canadian super heroes who wanted to prove that they had what it took to make it in the big leagues.

GAMMA FLIGHT
Initially a recruitment team for Alpha Flight, Gamma Flight became a temporary replacement team for Alpha Flight when they fell out of favour with the Canadian government. They later became the scientific research arm of Alpha Flight.

OMEGA FLIGHT
Omega Flight is a name that has been used by different teams of both heroes and villains. The original team was comprised of villains who fought Alpha Flight, but the most recent team were heroes who were brought together to fill the gap left when Alpha Flight temporarily disbanded.

NEVERLAND
This mutant concentration camp was also used as a recruitment centre for Weapon X operatives. Over six thousand mutants are believed to have been killed in Neverland, many of whom were executed when the camp was shut down.

DEPARTMENT H HEADQUARTERS (OTTAWA)
Department H was the branch of the Canadian government that dealt with superhumans. The first facility was in Ottawa, and it was from here that Wolverine was sent to tackle the Hulk.

DEPARTMENT H HEADQUARTERS (TORONTO)
The second Department H headquarters is a hi-tech advanced building from which Canada's superhuman Alpha Flight operated for a time.

FIRST MEETING OF HULK AND WOLVERINE
Logan was sent by Department H to Quebec to track a rampaging Bruce Banner. The two ended up fighting. Wolverine and Hulk have been trying to find out who is tougher ever since.

WOLVERINE

HE'S THE BEST AT WHAT HE DOES, BUT WHAT HE DOES ISN'T VERY NICE. WOLVERINE HAS SPENT MUCH OF HIS LIFE MAKING AMENDS FOR HIS TORTURED PAST. DESPITE BEING A PROFESSED LONER, LOGAN HAS BEEN A MEMBER OF MANY SUPER HERO TEAMS, INCLUDING THE X-MEN, THE AVENGERS, ALPHA FLIGHT AND X-FORCE.

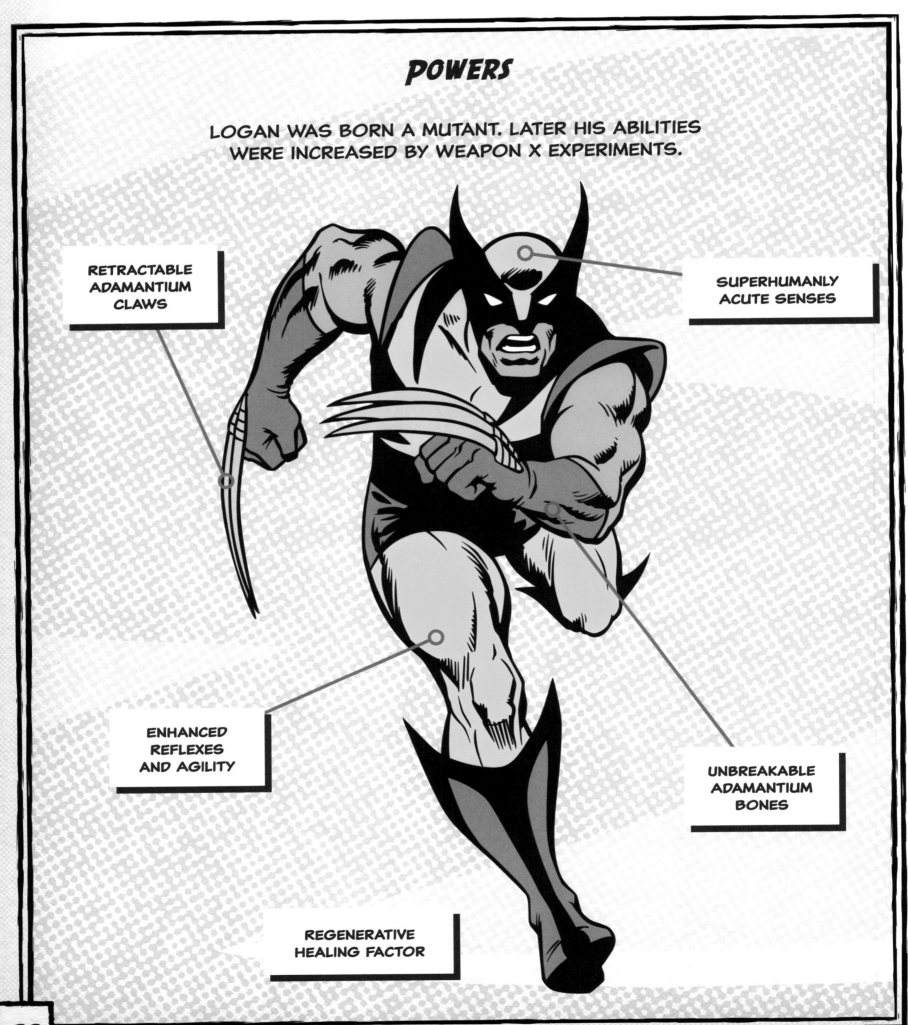

POWERS

LOGAN WAS BORN A MUTANT. LATER HIS ABILITIES WERE INCREASED BY WEAPON X EXPERIMENTS.

RETRACTABLE ADAMANTIUM CLAWS

SUPERHUMANLY ACUTE SENSES

ENHANCED REFLEXES AND AGILITY

UNBREAKABLE ADAMANTIUM BONES

REGENERATIVE HEALING FACTOR

WOLVERINE'S HISTORY

WOLVERINE'S MUTANT HEALING FACTOR MEANS THAT HE AGES ABNORMALLY SLOWLY. HE HAS BEEN ALIVE FOR MORE THAN A CENTURY, AND DURING THAT TIME HIS LIFE HAS TAKEN MANY TWISTS AND TURNS.

CHILDHOOD
Wolverine was born James Howlett and grew up in the Howlett estate in Alberta, Canada. His mother was Elizabeth Howlett, and his real father is believed to have been Thomas Logan, the groundskeeper of the estate. When James's mutant powers surfaced in the form of bone claws popping from his hands, he fled the estate in terror.

MERCENARY
James Howlett took the name Logan and travelled Canada, working as a miner and later a mercenary. During World War II he fought alongside key heroes including Blade, Black Widow, Nick Fury and Captain America.

JAPAN
After World War II Logan settled in Japan, where he fell in love with a woman called Itsu. While she was pregnant, she was killed by the Winter Soldier. Wolverine never knew, but his son, Daken, grew up to be an amoral killer who vowed revenge on his father for leaving him.

WEAPON X
Years later, Logan was captured by the clandestine US government Weapon X Project. Unbreakable Adamantium was bonded to his bones and claws, and he was brainwashed into thinking he was a mindless murderer. He escaped, but the mental scars never left him.

DEPARTMENT H
James and Heather Hudson found Wolverine after he escaped Weapon X and helped him slowly recover. He joined the Canadian super hero agency Department H, and was sent to apprehend the Hulk.

THE X-MEN
Wolverine was part of the new team of X-Men assembled by Professor Xavier to rescue the original X-Men from the island of Krakoa. Logan eventually found a home in the X-Men that he had never found before, and has been a part of the team in some form ever since.

X-23
Years later, Wolverine met a young female clone of himself called Laura Kinney, codenamed X-23. He recognised her feral nature and persuaded her to join the X-Men despite her reservations.

CENTRAL AND SOUTH AMERICA

SOUTH AMERICA CONTAINS SOME OF THE GREATEST LOST TREASURES ON EARTH. THE ANDES MOUNTAINS ARE HOME TO EL DORADO, THE FABLED CITY OF GOLD, AND WERE ALSO HOME BASE TO GALAXY-HOPPING CELESTIALS. THE SUPER VILLAIN ORGANISATION A.I.M. HAS BASES ALL OVER THE WORLD, BUT A.I.M. ISLAND IS FOUND IN THE CARIBBEAN, OFF SOUTH AMERICA.

THE TIMELINE OF A·I·M·

ADVANCED IDEA MECHANICS (BETTER KNOWN AS A.I.M.) IS AN ORGANISATION OF SCIENTISTS WHO CAN BE RECOGNISED BY THEIR SIGNATURE YELLOW OUTFITS, OFTEN REFERRED TO AS "BEE-KEEPER SUITS".

WORLD WAR II
A.I.M.'s origins can be traced back to World War II when Baron von Strucker brought a group of scientists together to provide weapons for Hydra.

SUPER VILLAINS
After World War II, A.I.M. set itself up as a weapons development organisation, trading advanced technology for power. A.I.M. has been battling S.H.I.E.L.D. for years, with new and more dangerous technologies being invented every day.

M.O.D.O.K.
One of A.I.M.'s deadliest creations is M.O.D.O.K., the Mental Organism Designed Only for Killing. M.O.D.O.K. was once a scientist called George Tarleton who was subjected to an experimental procedure and became a hyper intelligent being.

GOING "LEGITIMATE"
A.I.M. eventually went public, setting itself up on the island of Barbuda in an effort to gain diplomatic immunity. This was all a prelude to an attack on the United States, which was foiled by the Avengers.

COSTA VERDE
The Avengers helped stop a coup attempted by the Living Laser, who had been hired by the revolutionary Rodrigo Valdez, in the Central American country of Costa Verde.

DELVADIA
Delvadia is the birthplace of several super humans, including Anton Miguel Rodriquez, the Tarantula. The Tarantula was a freedom fighter who rose up against the fascist government, but who lost support over his extreme tactics.

EL DORADO
The mythical lost City of Gold is hidden deep in the Andes mountains. It contained the Sacred Flame of Life, which was actually a weapon created long ago by the Deviant race.

CITY OF THE SPACE GODS
Celestials landed on Earth thousands of years ago, and native Incans built a network of temples to honour them. The city contains a cosmic beacon, a cosmic door and a resurrection chamber.

BOCA CALIENTE
The villainous A.I.M. organisation forcibly took over this Caribbean island. Also known as A.I.M. Island, this base was used for arms trading and weapons research.

BARBUDA
The second A.I.M. Island was Barbuda in the Caribbean. A.I.M. can control the flow of time on the island, creating a technologically advanced civilisation.

NOVA ROMA
Nova Roma is a lost colony of descendants of the Roman Empire, hidden deep in the Amazon Jungle of Brazil.

SANTO MARCO
Magneto and the Brotherhood of Evil Mutants took over the Amazon country of Santo Marco. Later it was controlled by the mutant-hating President Emilio Duarte.

BARON ZEMO'S CASTLE
Heinrich Zemo fled Germany after World War II, and hid in a base in the Amazon jungle. This fortress was used as a headquarters for Zemo's Masters of Evil team.

RUSSIA

ALTHOUGH RUSSIAN-AMERICAN RELATIONS HAVE BEEN STRAINED OVER THE YEARS, SOME OF THE BRAVEST HEROES IN THE WORLD HAVE COME FROM RUSSIA. COLOSSUS AND MAGIK FROM THE X-MEN ARE BOTH FROM A COLLECTIVE FARM IN SIBERIA, AND NATASHA ROMANOFF TRAINED TO BECOME THE BLACK WIDOW IN THE RED ROOM ACADEMY.

THE RED ROOM ACADEMY
The Red Room turns women into remorseless assassins as part of Department X's espionage agenda. Natasha Romanoff is one of the graduates of the Black Widow programme.

KHYSTYM
The town of Khystym was destroyed and utterly irradiated in a nuclear explosion. Now known as the Dead Zone or the Forbidden Zone, it has become the home to radiation-based super villains.

THE REPUBLIC OF SLORENIA
Slorenia is still recovering from multiple horrific super villain attacks. The Republic is in a near-perpetual state of civil war, despite intervention from the international community.

RUMEKISTAN
The Flag Smasher took control of this country, but was assassinated by Domino. After he died, Cable worked hard to help install a leadership that was beneficial to the people of Rumekistan.

VOROZHEKIA
Once part of the Soviet Union, Vorozhekia became an independent republic which was governed by Ivan Druig, who is secretly Druig of the Eternals.

SUPER-SOLDIER SCHOOL
Professor Piotr Phobos was given the task of creating a school to train mutants, but instead used technology to steal their powers to power himself.

UST-ORDYNSKY COLLECTIVE FARM
Piotr and Illyana Rasputin were born in the Ust-Ordynsky Collective Farm near Lake Baikal in Siberia. Colossus once publicly manifested his powers, saving his sister from a runaway tractor.

RED GUARDIAN

THE RED GUARDIAN IDENTITY WAS CREATED TO BE THE SOVIET EQUIVALENT OF CAPTAIN AMERICA. MANY DIFFERENT SUPERHUMANS HAVE USED THE RED GUARDIAN IDENTITY, SUCH AS:

ALEKSEY LEBEDEV
After rescuing a woman and her infant from a burning building, Aleksey Lebedev was admitted to the USSR's Super-Soldier programme, becoming Red Guardian in 1941. He served until his death in the 1950s.

ALEXI SHOSTAKOV
Black Widow's husband faked his own death and took the identity of Red Guardian. He later fought the Avengers, but was believed killed saving Black Widow, his survival kept secret by Russian authorities.

TANIA BELINSKAYA
One of the few Red Guardians with actual super powers, Tania Belinskaya can store and redirect nuclear energy. Belinskaya later gave up the Red Guardian identity and became Starlight.

JOSEF PETKUS
Petkus is a Soviet Super-Soldier who later started calling himself the Steel Guardian instead of the Red Guardian.

NIKOLAI KRYLENKO
The current Red Guardian is the Soviet hero formerly known as Vanguard. Krylenko now uses a Vibranium shield and Red Guardian armour.

BLACK WIDOW

DESPITE BEING A MAJOR SUPER HERO, MUCH OF NATASHA ROMANOFF'S PAST IS STILL A MYSTERY. PART OF BEING ONE OF THE GREATEST SECRET AGENTS IN THE WORLD MEANS THAT BLACK WIDOW PLAYS HER CARDS VERY CLOSE TO HER CHEST. DESPITE HER EARLY YEARS AS A VILLAIN, BLACK WIDOW IS A TRUSTED AVENGER AND A TOP-LEVEL S.H.I.E.L.D. AGENT.

POWERS

NATALIA ALIANOVNA ROMANOVA (OR THE FAMILIAR/ANGLICISED NATASHA ROMANOFF) WAS ORPHANED AT A YOUNG AGE AND WAS EVENTUALLY RECRUITED BY THE USSR'S BLACK WIDOW PROGRAMME, WHERE SHE WAS CONDITIONED AS A DEADLY ESPIONAGE AGENT.

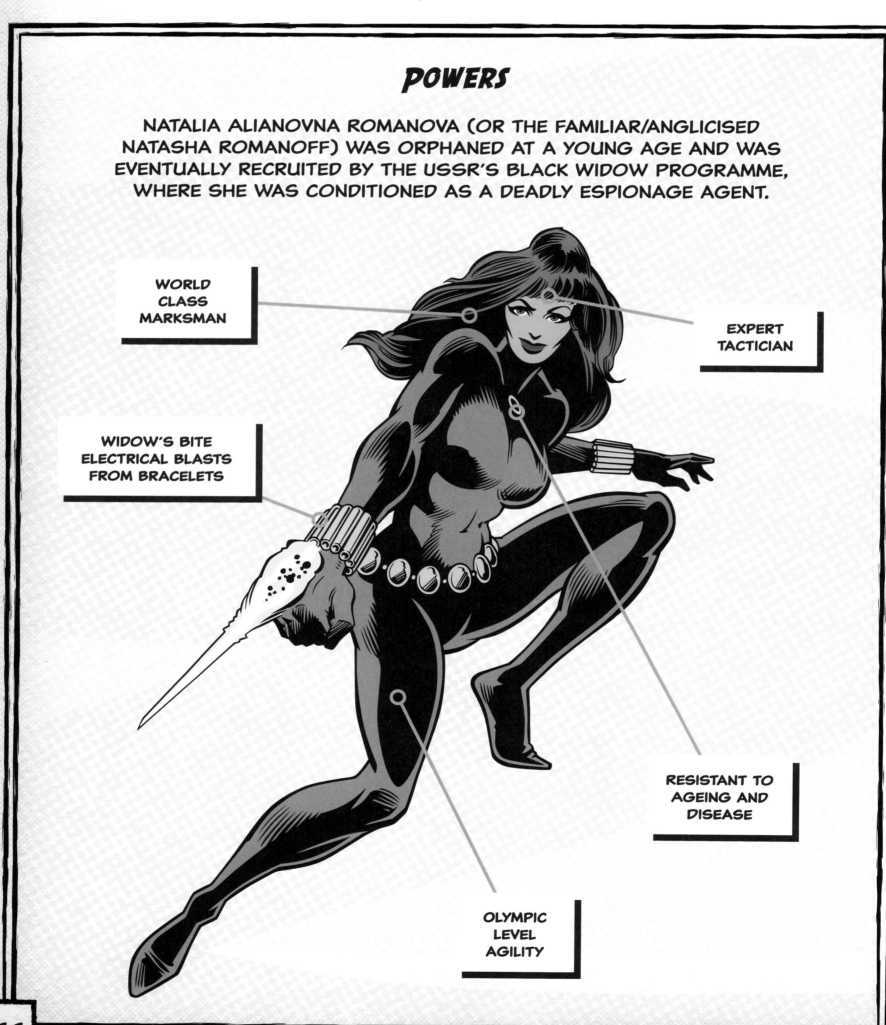

WORLD CLASS MARKSMAN

EXPERT TACTICIAN

WIDOW'S BITE ELECTRICAL BLASTS FROM BRACELETS

RESISTANT TO AGEING AND DISEASE

OLYMPIC LEVEL AGILITY

THE RED ROOM
Natasha was trained in the covert Red Room facility, a branch of Department X, the KGB's experimental science division. She was subjected to procedures that slowed her ageing process and enhanced her physical strength. She was also given intense espionage training and brainwashed into following orders.

KGB
Natasha married Alexi Shostakov, but he faked his death and became the Red Guardian. She joined the KGB and became a top operative. She clashed with Iron Man and the Avengers many times, manipulating Hawkeye into attacking the Avengers.

AVENGER AND S.H.I.E.L.D. AGENT
Eventually Natasha was able to shake off her Soviet brainwashing and asked to defect to the USA during World War II. Nick Fury used her as a S.H.I.E.L.D. agent for years before she joined the Avengers, becoming a trusted member and eventually a team leader.

YELENA BELOVA
Yelena was trained in the same Black Widow ops program as Natasha. She has attacked the Avengers several times.

LOCATIONS

THE RED ROOM

MOSCOW

MADRIPOOR

SAN FRANCISCO MANSION

S.H.I.E.L.D. HELICARRIER

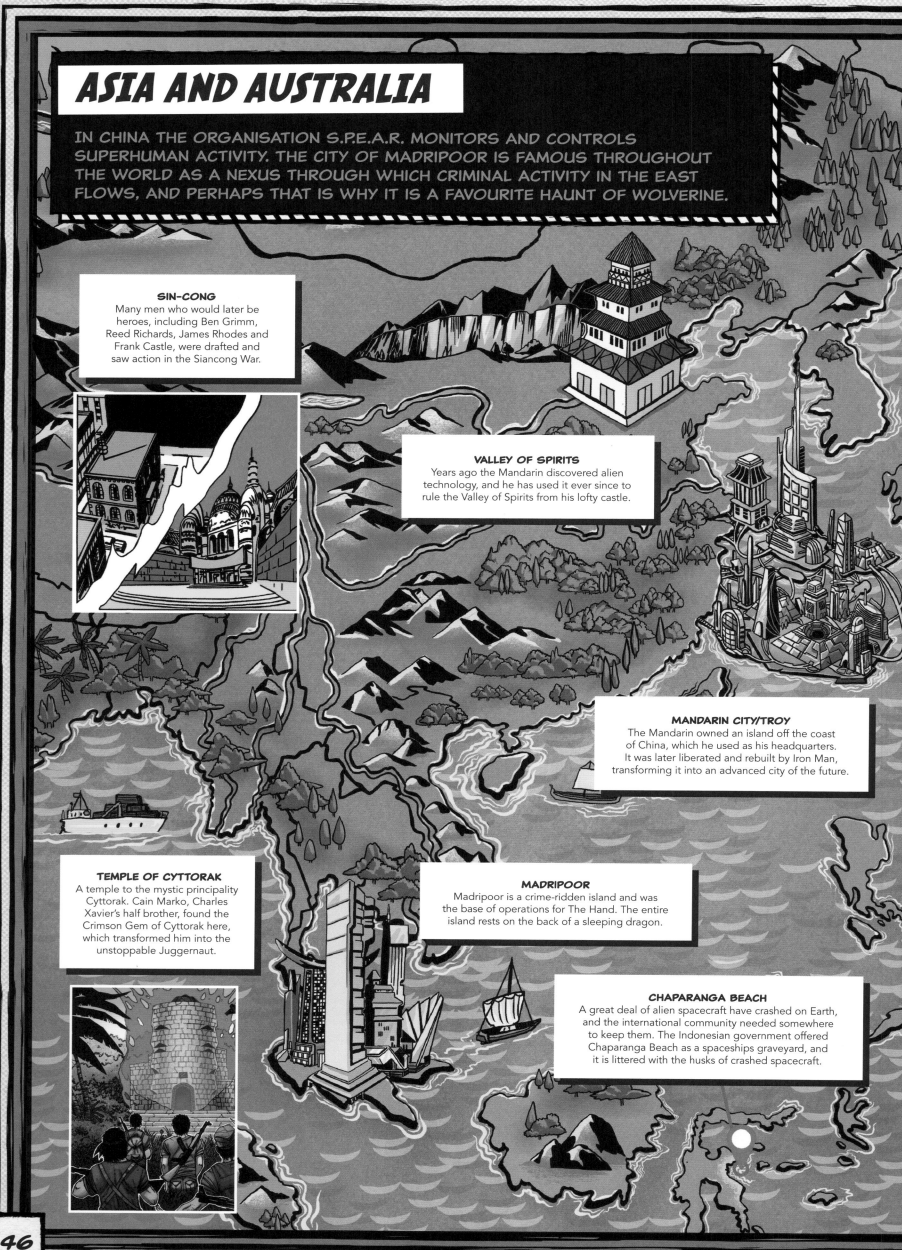

ASIA AND AUSTRALIA

IN CHINA THE ORGANISATION S.P.E.A.R. MONITORS AND CONTROLS SUPERHUMAN ACTIVITY. THE CITY OF MADRIPOOR IS FAMOUS THROUGHOUT THE WORLD AS A NEXUS THROUGH WHICH CRIMINAL ACTIVITY IN THE EAST FLOWS, AND PERHAPS THAT IS WHY IT IS A FAVOURITE HAUNT OF WOLVERINE.

SIN-CONG
Many men who would later be heroes, including Ben Grimm, Reed Richards, James Rhodes and Frank Castle, were drafted and saw action in the Siancong War.

VALLEY OF SPIRITS
Years ago the Mandarin discovered alien technology, and he has used it ever since to rule the Valley of Spirits from his lofty castle.

MANDARIN CITY/TROY
The Mandarin owned an island off the coast of China, which he used as his headquarters. It was later liberated and rebuilt by Iron Man, transforming it into an advanced city of the future.

TEMPLE OF CYTTORAK
A temple to the mystic principality Cyttorak. Cain Marko, Charles Xavier's half brother, found the Crimson Gem of Cyttorak here, which transformed him into the unstoppable Juggernaut.

MADRIPOOR
Madripoor is a crime-ridden island and was the base of operations for The Hand. The entire island rests on the back of a sleeping dragon.

CHAPARANGA BEACH
A great deal of alien spacecraft have crashed on Earth, and the international community needed somewhere to keep them. The Indonesian government offered Chaparanga Beach as a spaceships graveyard, and it is littered with the husks of crashed spacecraft.

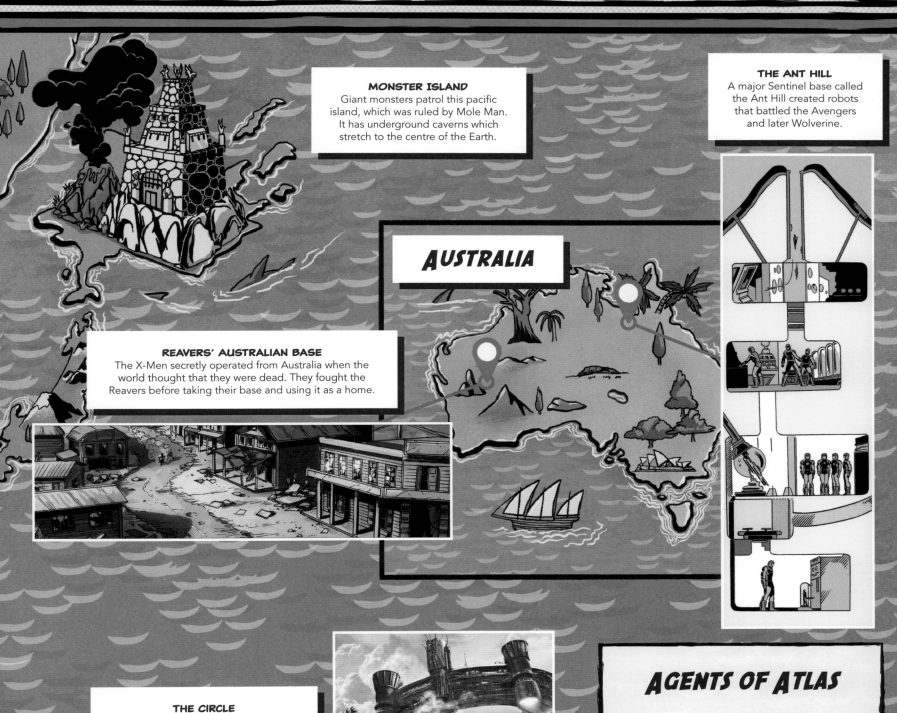

MONSTER ISLAND
Giant monsters patrol this pacific island, which was ruled by Mole Man. It has underground caverns which stretch to the centre of the Earth.

THE ANT HILL
A major Sentinel base called the Ant Hill created robots that battled the Avengers and later Wolverine.

AUSTRALIA

REAVERS' AUSTRALIAN BASE
The X-Men secretly operated from Australia when the world thought that they were dead. They fought the Reavers before taking their base and using it as a home.

THE CIRCLE
The headquarters of S.P.E.A.R., the Chinese equivalent of S.H.I.E.L.D., are found in a flying base known as the Circle. S.P.E.A.R.'s super hero team The Ascendants are also based in the Circle.

THE HELLFIRE ACADEMY SCHOOL FOR MUTANTS
Kade Kilgore set up the Hellfire Academy as a replacement for the decadent Hellfire Club, and recruited new students in a dark reflection of the Xavier Institute. It is located on an island in the Pacific Ocean.

AGENTS OF ATLAS

THE ATLAS FOUNDATION IS AN ANCIENT, POWERFUL SECRET SOCIETY THAT HAS BEEN GUIDING WORLD AFFAIRS FOR CENTURIES.

THE ATLAS FOUNDATION
One of the oldest secret societies in existence, the Atlas Foundation goes back as far as the time of Genghis Khan and the Mongol Empire, and has been using its vast resources to try to take over the world.

JIMMY WOO
Each leader of the Atlas Foundation chooses his successor. A former leader named Master Plan chose FBI agent Jimmy Woo, but instead of using the Atlas Foundation for evil, Jimmy Woo decided to be a force for good.

AGENTS OF ATLAS
Woo created the Agents of Atlas, a team of clandestine super heroes who kept their activities hidden from S.H.I.E.L.D. and the world at large.

THE AVENGERS

WHENEVER THERE IS A MOMENT OF GREAT NEED, THE EARTH'S MIGHTIEST HEROES COME TOGETHER TO DO THE IMPOSSIBLE. THOUGH THE LINEUP IS ALWAYS CHANGING, THE BRAVERY AND HEROISM DO NOT. THE AVENGERS' FAME HAS SPREAD SO FAR THROUGHOUT THE GALAXY THAT EARTH IS KNOWN TO SOME AS "AVENGERS WORLD".

ORIGINAL MEMBERS

THOR
THOR ODINSON
Norse God of Thunder

IRON MAN
TONY STARK
Advanced suit of armour

ANT-MAN
HANK PYM
Changes size, commands ants

WASP
JANET VAN DYNE
Changes size, flies

HULK
BRUCE BANNER
Green rage monster

KEY MEMBERS

CAPTAIN AMERICA
STEVE ROGERS
Super-Soldier

HAWKEYE
CLINT BARTON
Expert marksman

QUICKSILVER
PIETRO MAXIMOFF
Speedster

SCARLET WITCH
WANDA MAXIMOFF
Hex-casting sorcerer

HERCULES
Greek demigod

BLACK PANTHER
T'CHALLA
Advanced technology, enhanced physique

VISION
Advanced android, density control

BLACK WIDOW
NATASHA ROMANOFF
Top level espionage agent

BEAST
HANK MCCOY
Acrobatic, scientific genius

WONDER MAN
SIMON WILLIAMS
Ionic energy strength, durability

CAPTAIN MARVEL
CAROL DANVERS
Half-alien, flight, super-strength

FALCON
SAM WILSON
Avian telepathy and flight

SHE-HULK
JENNIFER WALTERS
Superhuman strength and endurance

SPECTRUM
MONICA RAMBEAU
Living energy

MOCKINGBIRD
BOBBI MORSE
Advanced martial arts training

WAR MACHINE
JAMES RHODES
Advanced Stark tech armoured suit

SUB-MARINER
NAMOR MCKENZIE
Amphibious King of the Seas

QUASAR
WENDELL VAUGHN
Cosmically-powered
Protector of the Universe

SPIDER-MAN
PETER PARKER
Spider-based powers
and web-shooters

ANT-MAN
SCOTT LANG
Size-changing
electronics expert

LUKE CAGE
Super strength,
unbreakable skin

WOLVERINE
LOGAN / JAMES HOWLETT
Adamantium bones and claws,
healing factor

SPIDER-WOMAN
JESSICA DREW
Spider-powered
detective, spy

DOCTOR STRANGE
STEPHEN STRANGE
Sorcerer Supreme

ROGUE
ANNA MARIE LEBEAU
Power absorption,
super-strength, flight

THOR
JANE FOSTER
Human Goddess
of Thunder

GHOST RIDER
ROBBIE REYES
Spirit of Vengeance

AVENGERS' BASES

AVENGERS MANSION
For years the Avengers' base in New York
was Avengers Mansion. It was filled with
Stark tech and had quarters for all members.

AVENGERS COMPOUND
This huge estate in LA is on the Pacific Coast
and was originally given to the Avengers as
a base for the West Coast Avengers team.
It is now a training ground for Avengers Academy.

AVENGERS TOWER
Tony Stark gave a section of Stark Tower to
the Avengers when the Avengers Mansion
was destroyed by Scarlet Witch.

AVENGERS MOUNTAIN
This Avengers Headquarters is actually the
hollowed out body of a dead Celestial,
which is located at the North Pole.

INDIA, PAKISTAN AND THE MIDDLE EAST

THE AREA AROUND THE HIMALAYAN MOUNTAINS HAS BEEN AN IMPORTANT PLACE FOR SUPER HEROES FOR YEARS. STEPHEN STRANGE TRAINED IN THE ART OF MAGIC IN KAMAR-TAJ AND DOCTOR DOOM HAD HIS MAGICAL ARMOUR CREATED IN A MONASTERY HERE.

CAIRO
Ororo Munroe lived on the streets of Cairo in her youth and became a thief and pickpocket of exceptional skill. She once crossed Charles Xavier's path when she picked his pocket, but escaped his psychic hold when he was attacked by the evil Shadow King. Munroe would be recruited into the X-Men by Xavier years later.

TRANS-SABAL
Civil war has gripped Trans-Sabal for years, and despite super hero intervention by the Hulk, X-Factor, New Warriors and others, the area remained extremely politically volatile.

MAZIKHANDAR
Seeking the revival of the Third Reich, the global terrorist network Axis Mundi began replacing key world leaders with bioengineered replicas, with Mazikhandarian President Hamzah Hasaan being one of the first. A modern incarnation of the Invaders opposed the Axis Mundi.

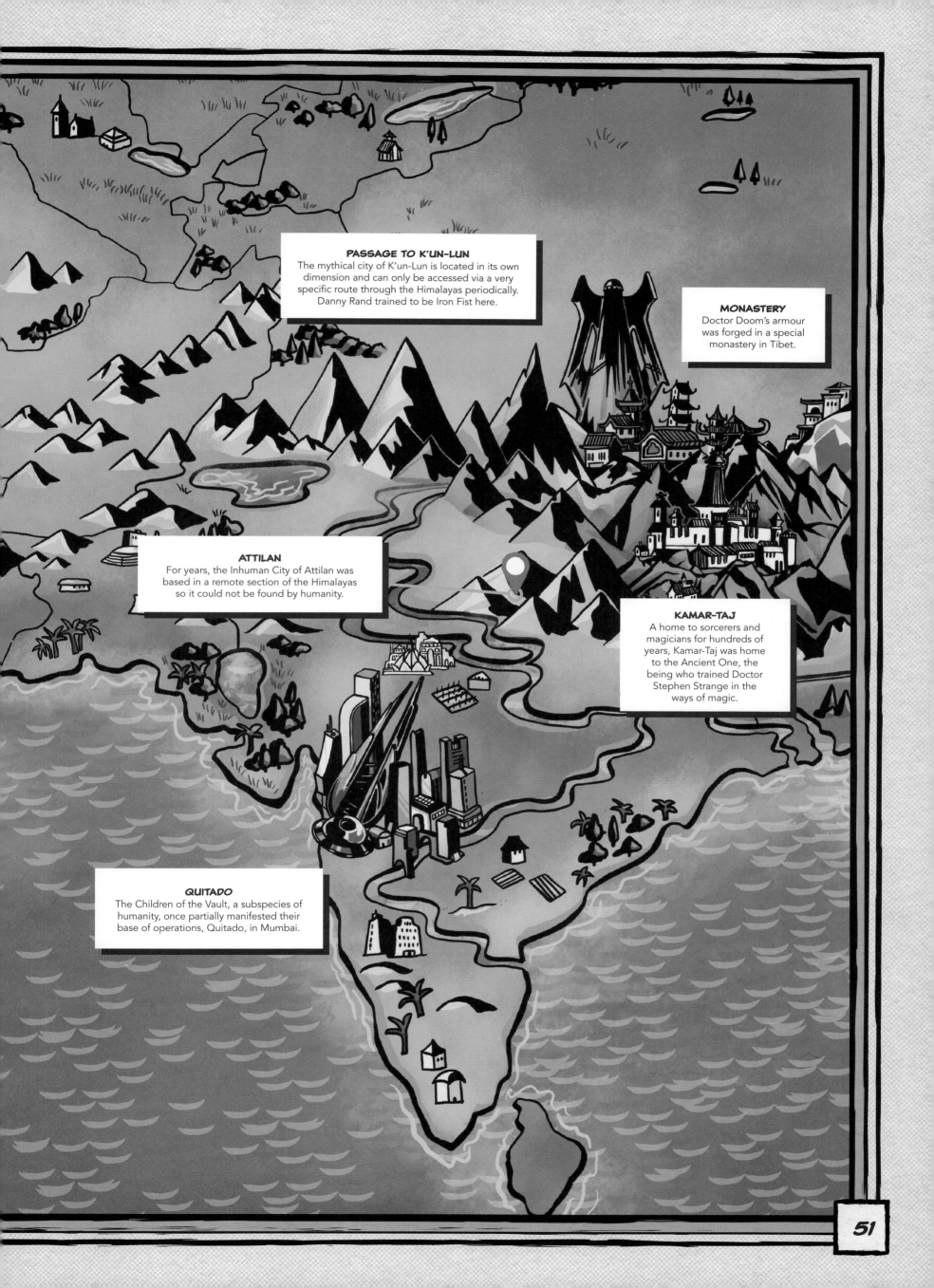

PASSAGE TO K'UN-LUN
The mythical city of K'un-Lun is located in its own dimension and can only be accessed via a very specific route through the Himalayas periodically. Danny Rand trained to be Iron Fist here.

MONASTERY
Doctor Doom's armour was forged in a special monastery in Tibet.

ATTILAN
For years, the Inhuman City of Attilan was based in a remote section of the Himalayas so it could not be found by humanity.

KAMAR-TAJ
A home to sorcerers and magicians for hundreds of years, Kamar-Taj was home to the Ancient One, the being who trained Doctor Stephen Strange in the ways of magic.

QUITADO
The Children of the Vault, a subspecies of humanity, once partially manifested their base of operations, Quitado, in Mumbai.

UNITED KINGDOM

DESPITE BEING A RELATIVELY SMALL ISLAND OFF THE COAST OF EUROPE, GREAT BRITAIN HAS HAD AN OVERSIZED SAY IN WORLD AFFAIRS. MANY SUPERHUMANS ARE BRITISH, INCLUDING BETSY BRADDOCK, BLADE, SPIDER-WOMAN AND MISTER SINISTER. APPOINTED BY KING ARTHUR'S MAGICIAN MERLIN, CAPTAIN BRITAIN PROTECTS THE BRITISH ISLES.

THE TRUE HISTORY OF MI:13

MI:13 (MILITARY INTELLIGENCE: SECTION 13) IS THE BRITISH AGENCY CREATED FOR PARANORMAL AND SUPERHUMAN AFFAIRS.

S.T.R.I.K.E., RCX, W.H.O.

S.T.R.I.K.E., RCX and the Weird Happenings Organisation (W.H.O.) were the predecessors of MI:13 in dealing with superhuman affairs.

PETE WISDOM

Mutant and ex X-Force member Pete Wisdom is the head of MI:13. Wisdom has the mutant ability to create hot knives from the end of his fingertips, but his real skill lies in spycraft and outthinking his opponents.

SKRULL INVASION

After the attempted Skrull invasion of the world, the Prime Minister passed a law drafting every super hero in the UK into MI:13.

MUIR ISLAND

Dr Moira MacTaggert runs the Mutant Research Centre from Muir Island in the Outer Hebrides. As a very important scientific research complex, it has been invaluable in helping the X-Men and other mutants.

CASSIDY KEEP

Sean Cassidy and his daughter Theresa (Banshee of the X-Men and Siryn of X-Factor Investigations) own the Cassidy ancestral home. Leprechauns and fairies have also been known to make Cassidy Keep their home.

STORMHAVEN CASTLE

Shang-Chi and Freelance Restorations worked from Stormhaven Castle in Scotland. Run by Sir Denis Nayland Smith (and later Black Jack Tarr), they fought against Shang-Chi's criminal mastermind father.

DARKMOOR

Darkmoor Energy Research Centre is based near a powerful mystical stone circle, and was used to create and monitor British super heroes.

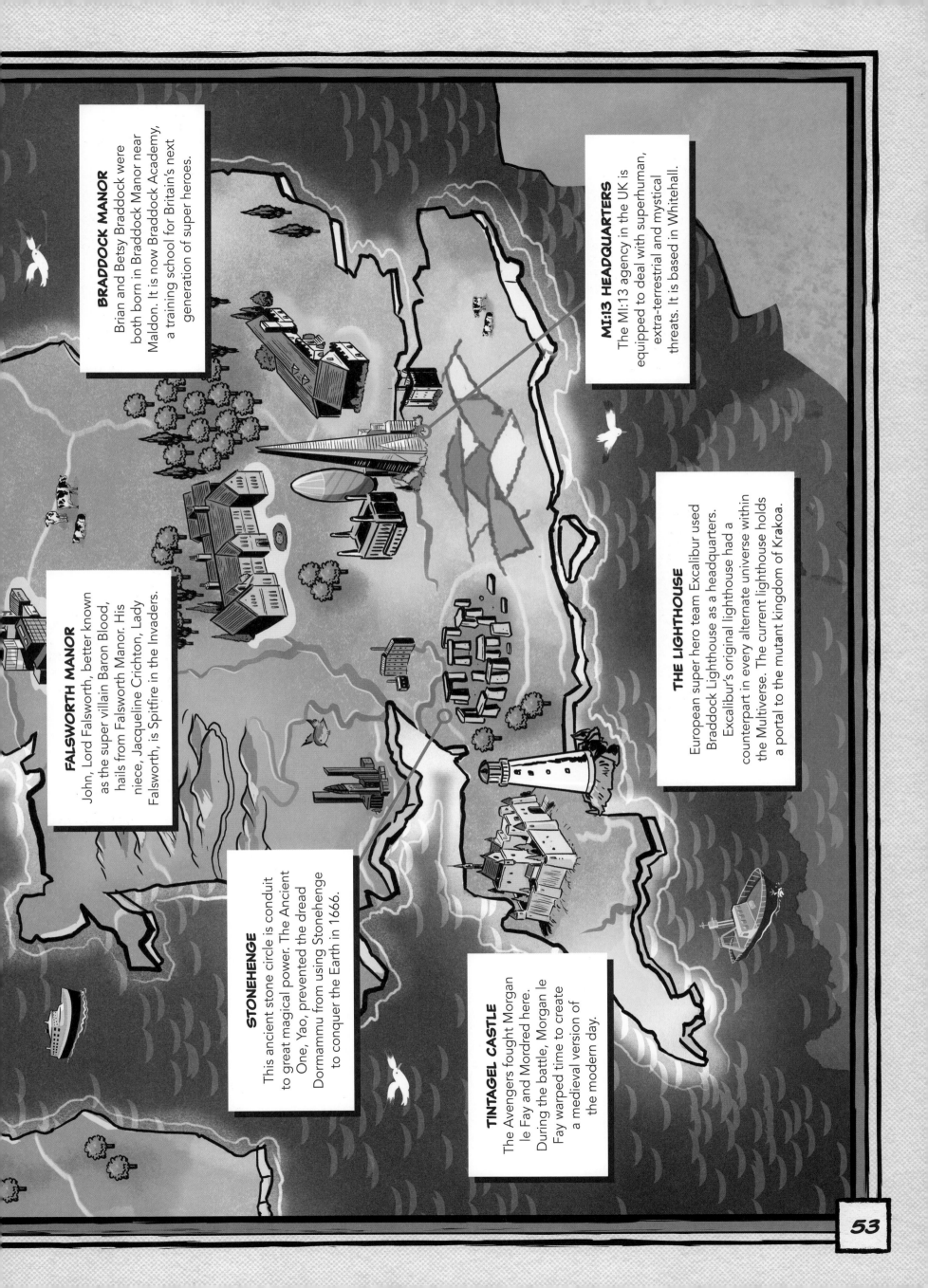

BRADDOCK MANOR

Brian and Betsy Braddock were both born in Braddock Manor near Maldon. It is now Braddock Academy, a training school for Britain's next generation of super heroes.

MI:13 HEADQUARTERS

The MI:13 agency in the UK is equipped to deal with superhuman, extra-terrestrial and mystical threats. It is based in Whitehall.

FALSWORTH MANOR

John, Lord Falsworth, better known as the super villain Baron Blood, hails from Falsworth Manor. His niece, Jacqueline Crichton, Lady Falsworth, is Spitfire in the Invaders.

THE LIGHTHOUSE

European super hero team Excalibur used Braddock Lighthouse as a headquarters. Excalibur's original lighthouse had a counterpart in every alternate universe within the Multiverse. The current lighthouse holds a portal to the mutant kingdom of Krakoa.

STONEHENGE

This ancient stone circle is conduit to great magical power. The Ancient One, Yao, prevented the dread Dormammu from using Stonehenge to conquer the Earth in 1666.

TINTAGEL CASTLE

The Avengers fought Morgan le Fay and Mordred here. During the battle, Morgan le Fay warped time to create a medieval version of the modern day.

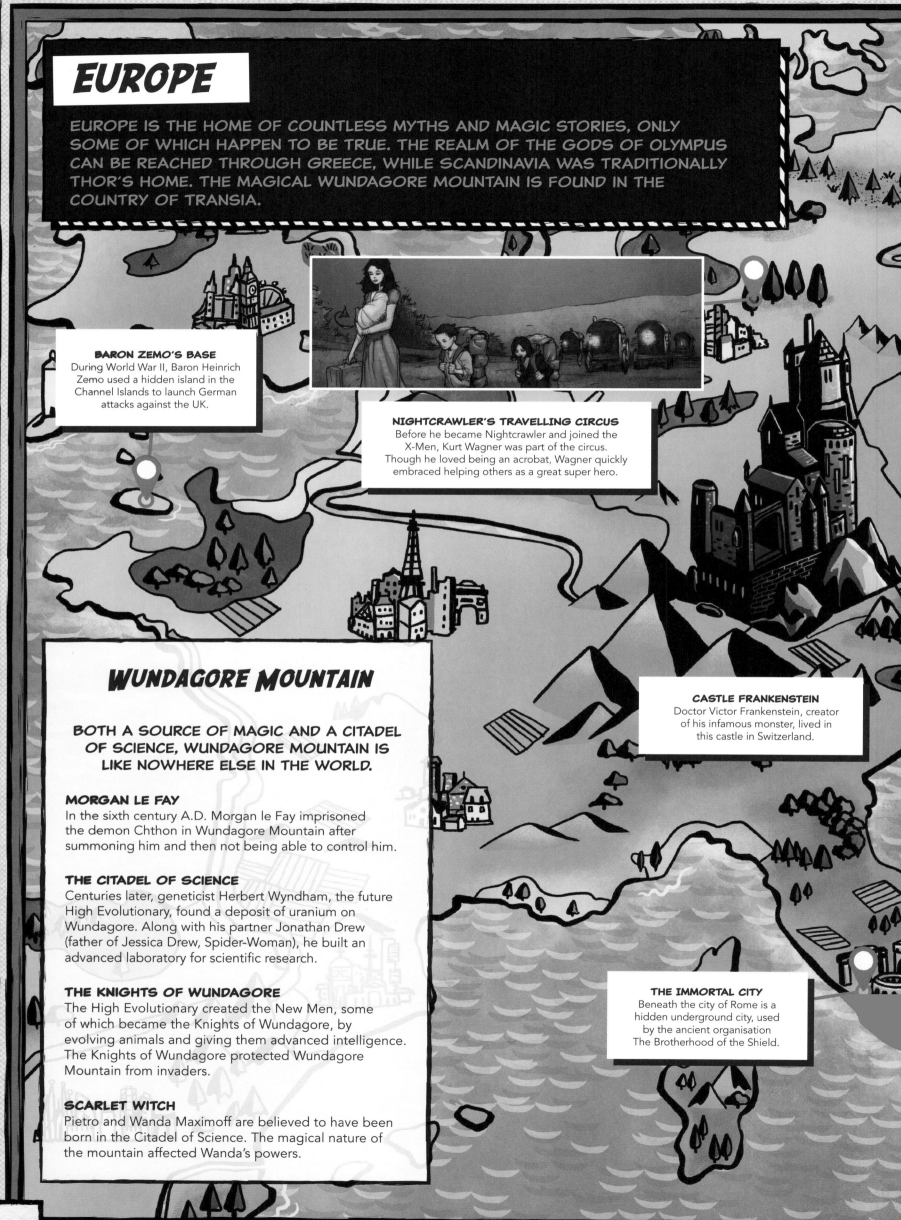

EUROPE

EUROPE IS THE HOME OF COUNTLESS MYTHS AND MAGIC STORIES, ONLY SOME OF WHICH HAPPEN TO BE TRUE. THE REALM OF THE GODS OF OLYMPUS CAN BE REACHED THROUGH GREECE, WHILE SCANDINAVIA WAS TRADITIONALLY THOR'S HOME. THE MAGICAL WUNDAGORE MOUNTAIN IS FOUND IN THE COUNTRY OF TRANSIA.

BARON ZEMO'S BASE
During World War II, Baron Heinrich Zemo used a hidden island in the Channel Islands to launch German attacks against the UK.

NIGHTCRAWLER'S TRAVELLING CIRCUS
Before he became Nightcrawler and joined the X-Men, Kurt Wagner was part of the circus. Though he loved being an acrobat, Wagner quickly embraced helping others as a great super hero.

CASTLE FRANKENSTEIN
Doctor Victor Frankenstein, creator of his infamous monster, lived in this castle in Switzerland.

THE IMMORTAL CITY
Beneath the city of Rome is a hidden underground city, used by the ancient organisation The Brotherhood of the Shield.

WUNDAGORE MOUNTAIN

BOTH A SOURCE OF MAGIC AND A CITADEL OF SCIENCE, WUNDAGORE MOUNTAIN IS LIKE NOWHERE ELSE IN THE WORLD.

MORGAN LE FAY
In the sixth century A.D. Morgan le Fay imprisoned the demon Chthon in Wundagore Mountain after summoning him and then not being able to control him.

THE CITADEL OF SCIENCE
Centuries later, geneticist Herbert Wyndham, the future High Evolutionary, found a deposit of uranium on Wundagore. Along with his partner Jonathan Drew (father of Jessica Drew, Spider-Woman), he built an advanced laboratory for scientific research.

THE KNIGHTS OF WUNDAGORE
The High Evolutionary created the New Men, some of which became the Knights of Wundagore, by evolving animals and giving them advanced intelligence. The Knights of Wundagore protected Wundagore Mountain from invaders.

SCARLET WITCH
Pietro and Wanda Maximoff are believed to have been born in the Citadel of Science. The magical nature of the mountain affected Wanda's powers.

MJÖLNIR'S CAVE
Doctor Donald Blake found Thor's hammer Mjölnir here, which transformed him into the Norse thunder god Thor. Donald Blake was later revealed to be a false identity, created to teach Thor humility. Thor spent much of the Middle Ages in Norway and Scandinavia, giving rise to legends of the Thunder God.

BAGALIA
Also known as the "Red Light Nation". Super villains have flocked to the nation of Bagalia, which is ruled by the Masters of Evil. The capital city is found at the bottom of a huge chasm.

KINGDOM OF SYMKARIA
Silver Sable runs her mercenary group the Wild Pack from her home country of Symkaria. The money made from the Wild Pack's missions is one of the exports that keeps the country's economy from collapsing.

CASTLE DRACULA
Count Vlad Dracula was born here in the 15th century and has lived there off-and-on ever since. The castle has seen many acts of unspeakable evil from Dracula and his vampire race.

REPUBLIC OF TRANSIA
Wanda and Pietro Maximoff were both born in Transia, the home of the mystical Mount Wundagore.

MOUNT OLYMPUS
The realm of Hercules and the other ancient Greek gods is traditionally reached through Mount Olympus in Greece.

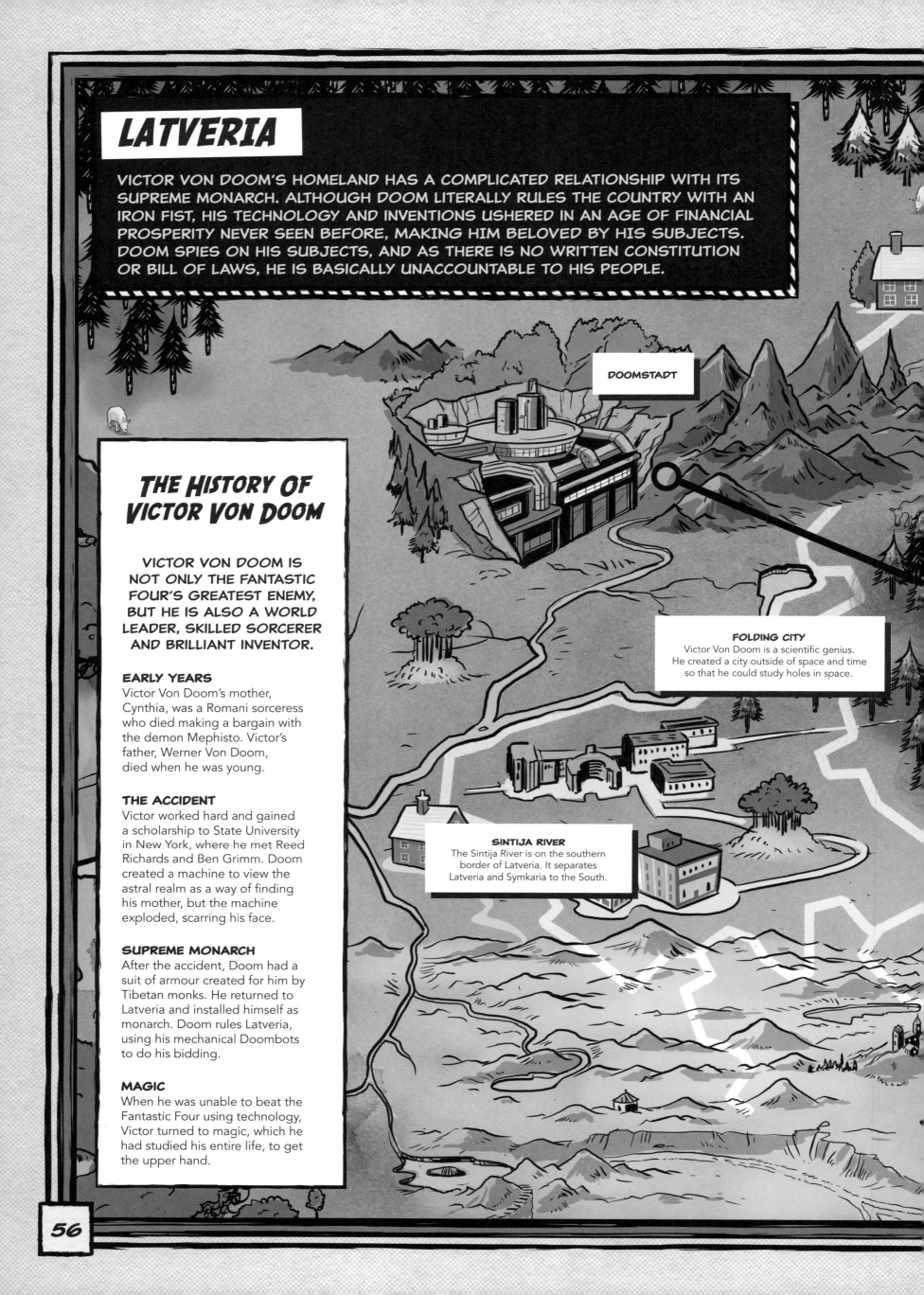

LATVERIA

VICTOR VON DOOM'S HOMELAND HAS A COMPLICATED RELATIONSHIP WITH ITS SUPREME MONARCH. ALTHOUGH DOOM LITERALLY RULES THE COUNTRY WITH AN IRON FIST, HIS TECHNOLOGY AND INVENTIONS USHERED IN AN AGE OF FINANCIAL PROSPERITY NEVER SEEN BEFORE, MAKING HIM BELOVED BY HIS SUBJECTS. DOOM SPIES ON HIS SUBJECTS, AND AS THERE IS NO WRITTEN CONSTITUTION OR BILL OF LAWS, HE IS BASICALLY UNACCOUNTABLE TO HIS PEOPLE.

THE HISTORY OF VICTOR VON DOOM

VICTOR VON DOOM IS NOT ONLY THE FANTASTIC FOUR'S GREATEST ENEMY, BUT HE IS ALSO A WORLD LEADER, SKILLED SORCERER AND BRILLIANT INVENTOR.

EARLY YEARS
Victor Von Doom's mother, Cynthia, was a Romani sorceress who died making a bargain with the demon Mephisto. Victor's father, Werner Von Doom, died when he was young.

THE ACCIDENT
Victor worked hard and gained a scholarship to State University in New York, where he met Reed Richards and Ben Grimm. Doom created a machine to view the astral realm as a way of finding his mother, but the machine exploded, scarring his face.

SUPREME MONARCH
After the accident, Doom had a suit of armour created for him by Tibetan monks. He returned to Latveria and installed himself as monarch. Doom rules Latveria, using his mechanical Doombots to do his bidding.

MAGIC
When he was unable to beat the Fantastic Four using technology, Victor turned to magic, which he had studied his entire life, to get the upper hand.

DOOMSTADT

FOLDING CITY
Victor Von Doom is a scientific genius. He created a city outside of space and time so that he could study holes in space.

SINTIJA RIVER
The Sintija River is on the southern border of Latveria. It separates Latveria and Symkaria to the South.

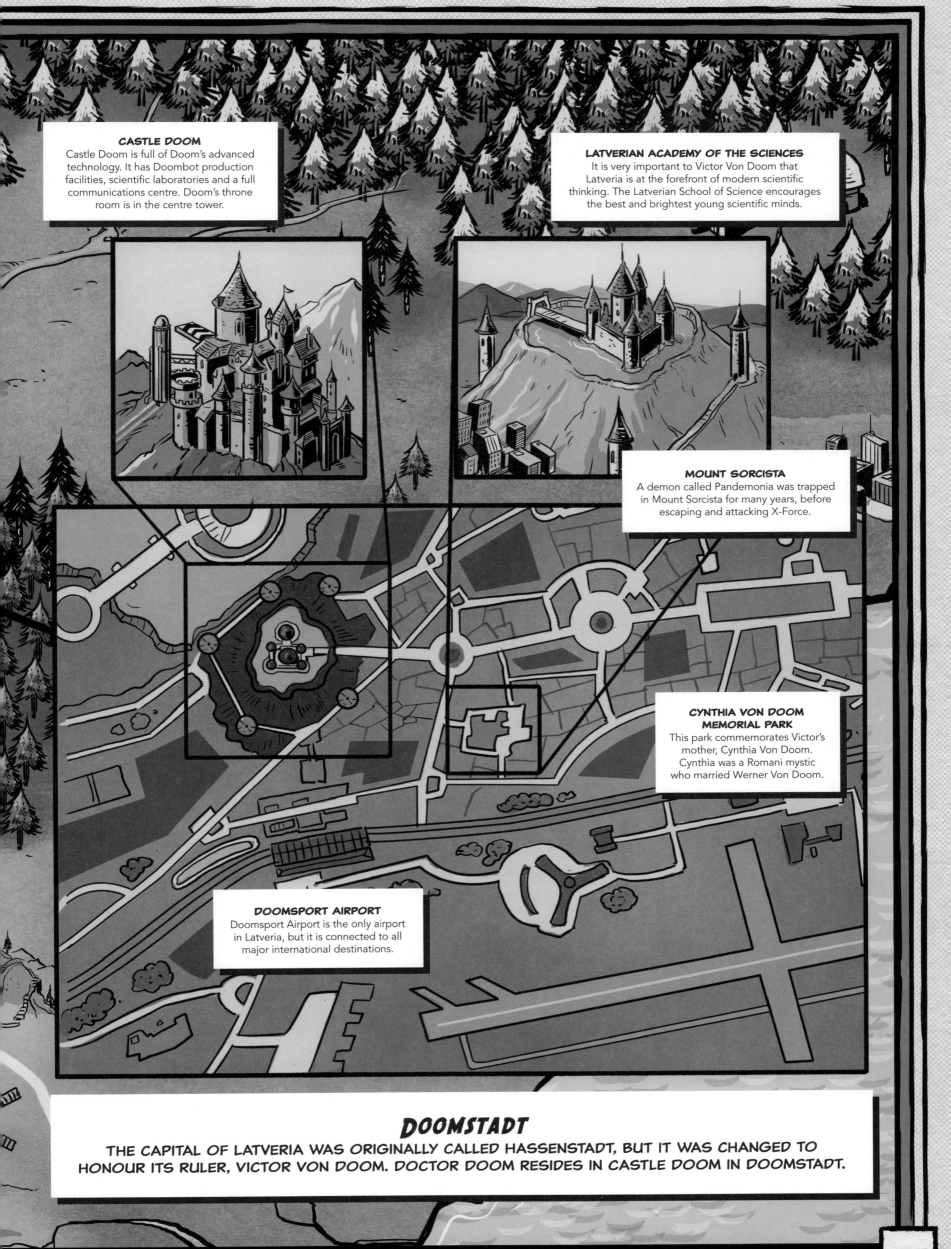

CASTLE DOOM
Castle Doom is full of Doom's advanced technology. It has Doombot production facilities, scientific laboratories and a full communications centre. Doom's throne room is in the centre tower.

LATVERIAN ACADEMY OF THE SCIENCES
It is very important to Victor Von Doom that Latveria is at the forefront of modern scientific thinking. The Latverian School of Science encourages the best and brightest young scientific minds.

MOUNT SORCISTA
A demon called Pandemonia was trapped in Mount Sorcista for many years, before escaping and attacking X-Force.

CYNTHIA VON DOOM MEMORIAL PARK
This park commemorates Victor's mother, Cynthia Von Doom. Cynthia was a Romani mystic who married Werner Von Doom.

DOOMSPORT AIRPORT
Doomsport Airport is the only airport in Latveria, but it is connected to all major international destinations.

DOOMSTADT
THE CAPITAL OF LATVERIA WAS ORIGINALLY CALLED HASSENSTADT, BUT IT WAS CHANGED TO HONOUR ITS RULER, VICTOR VON DOOM. DOCTOR DOOM RESIDES IN CASTLE DOOM IN DOOMSTADT.

THE SAVAGE LAND AND PANGEA

HIDDEN DEEP IN ANTARCTICA IS THE SAVAGE LAND, A LAND LOST TO TIME. THIS PREHISTORIC PRESERVE IS FILLED WITH DINOSAURS AND OTHER WONDERS OF EVOLUTION. THE SAVAGE LAND WAS CREATED BY ALIEN RACES AS A WAY TO OBSERVE EVOLUTION, BUT THIS EVOLUTIONARY PROGRESS WAS ALTERED BY ANCIENT ATLANTEANS.

MARGUERITE BAY
This bay on the west side of the Antarctic Peninsula provides a treacherous crossing to the Savage Land.

SKULL ISLAND
This island takes its name from a distinctive rock formation that looks like a skull. This island has been used as a refuge against Swamp People and pirates.

TRIBES OF THE SAVAGE LAND

HUMANS AND HOMINIDS
The Savage Land is home to many different tribes of humans and Neanderthals. Ka-Zar befriended a saber-toothed tiger called Zabu after he saved him from being killed by primitive Man-Apes.

BEAST-MEN
Ancient Atlanteans created various races of human/beast hybrids, including the winged Pterons. Other tribes are believed to have evolved from dinosaurs.

SAVAGE LAND MUTATES
Magneto subjected Savage Land natives to radiation, creating a new race of genetically altered mutants.

WAR ROOM X
Magneto has relocated to the Savage Land as a base more than once. The latest time was when Magneto led a team of lethal mutants in protecting mutantkind at any cost.

SAURON'S CITADEL
The super villain Sauron made the Savage Land his home after he was bitten by mutated pterodactyls and eventually transformed into a pterodactyl-like creature.

ALTAR OF DEATH
The Swamp Men used this to sacrifice enemies to their gods. Ka-Zar was brought here, but managed to escape.

DINOSAUR GRAVEYARD
Dinosaurs never died out in the Savage Land. Many species still exist, while others have evolved and mutated into new creatures.

KA-ZAR'S HOME
Ka-Zar was born Kevin Plunder, the son of a British Explorer. He grew up in the Savage Land and is its protector.

HAUK'KA CITY
The Hauk'ka are a race of humanoid dinosaurs who are descended from dinosaurs. They are as technologically and culturally advanced as humans and are ruled by a council of Elders.

CITY OF SICKLES
This ancient city was built thousands of years ago by a death cult as a place to sacrifice victims to Jhoatun Lau, the Marrow God. More recently other cultists, including the Hand, have entered the city.

AVENGER BASE TWO
This camouflaged dome in the Savage Land was the secret home of Bobby DaCosta's rebranded A.I.M. organisation, called Avengers Idea Mechanics.

ATLANTIS

TWENTY THOUSAND YEARS AGO THE EMPIRE OF ATLANTIS WAS THE MOST HIGHLY ADVANCED CIVILISATION THE WORLD HAS EVER SEEN. NOW SUNK BENEATH THE WAVES, ATLANTIS IS A WATERY REFLECTION OF ITS FORMER GLORY. ALTANTEANS KNOWN AS *HOMO MERMANUS* CAN BREATHE UNDERWATER.

SEAREBRO
A team of X-Men led by Jean Grey operated out of a sub-aquatic headquarters for a time, one named Searebro, a pun on the name of the X-Men's mutant locating computer Cerebro.

HYDROBASE/AVENGERS ISLAND
Once the lair of supervillain Doctor Hydro, this later became the home for the Avengers for a time after the Avengers Mansion was destroyed.

NEW ATLANTIS
Atlantis has been destroyed more than once, but has always been rebuilt. Shown here is an iteration of Atlantis built to support the mutant nation of Utopia off the coast of San Francisco when the mutant and Atlantean races were allied for a time.

KINGDOM OF LEMURIA
Lemuria was once a powerful civilisation, but it sunk beneath the waves. It was the centre of the Deviant Empire.

NAMOR'S UNDERSEA VILLA
When he was not the ruler of Atlantis, Namor needed somewhere to live.

KADESH BASE
The technologically-advanced undersea base of the Blue Marvel.

THA-KORR
The city of Tha-Korr is named after Emperor Thakorr, Namor's grandfather. The city was once the heart of the old Empire, but was abandoned. It was later used by Attuma and his horde.

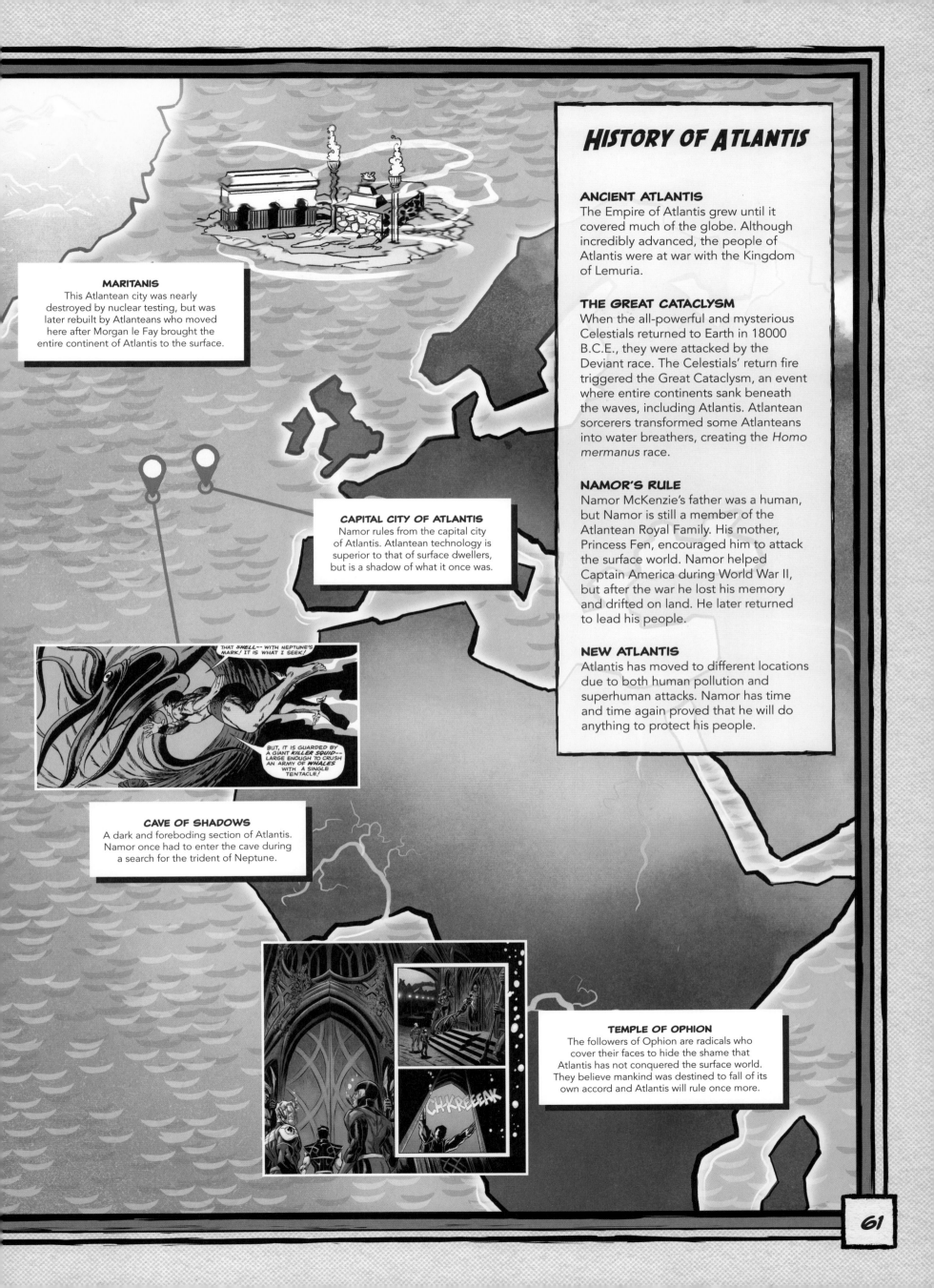

HISTORY OF ATLANTIS

ANCIENT ATLANTIS
The Empire of Atlantis grew until it covered much of the globe. Although incredibly advanced, the people of Atlantis were at war with the Kingdom of Lemuria.

THE GREAT CATACLYSM
When the all-powerful and mysterious Celestials returned to Earth in 18000 B.C.E., they were attacked by the Deviant race. The Celestials' return fire triggered the Great Cataclysm, an event where entire continents sank beneath the waves, including Atlantis. Atlantean sorcerers transformed some Atlanteans into water breathers, creating the *Homo mermanus* race.

NAMOR'S RULE
Namor McKenzie's father was a human, but Namor is still a member of the Atlantean Royal Family. His mother, Princess Fen, encouraged him to attack the surface world. Namor helped Captain America during World War II, but after the war he lost his memory and drifted on land. He later returned to lead his people.

NEW ATLANTIS
Atlantis has moved to different locations due to both human pollution and superhuman attacks. Namor has time and time again proved that he will do anything to protect his people.

MARITANIS
This Atlantean city was nearly destroyed by nuclear testing, but was later rebuilt by Atlanteans who moved here after Morgan le Fay brought the entire continent of Atlantis to the surface.

CAPITAL CITY OF ATLANTIS
Namor rules from the capital city of Atlantis. Atlantean technology is superior to that of surface dwellers, but is a shadow of what it once was.

CAVE OF SHADOWS
A dark and foreboding section of Atlantis. Namor once had to enter the cave during a search for the trident of Neptune.

TEMPLE OF OPHION
The followers of Ophion are radicals who cover their faces to hide the shame that Atlantis has not conquered the surface world. They believe mankind was destined to fall of its own accord and Atlantis will rule once more.

KRAKOA

KRAKOA IS A LIVING ISLAND THAT RESIDES IN THE PACIFIC OCEAN. THE ORIGINAL TEAM OF X-MEN WERE CAPTURED BY KRAKOA, AND PROFESSOR XAVIER SENT TWO TEAMS OF X-MEN AFTER THEM. PROFESSOR X MADE PEACE WITH KRAKOA, AND NOW THE ISLAND SERVES AS A SOVEREIGN NATION STATE FOR MUTANTS. THE FLOWERS OF KRAKOA ALLOW MUTANTS TO TELEPORT TO THE ISLAND FROM ANYWHERE ANOTHER FLOWER GATE HAS BEEN GROWN IN THE UNIVERSE.

BAR SINISTER
Mister Sinister and his clones have created their own nightclub on Krakoa. They deal in information and gossip.

ORACLE
The underground home of Mystique

TRANSIT
Mutants can use the flowers of Krakoa to travel to Krakoa from anywhere in the world, or beyond.

ARENA
A coliseum used to perform the Crucible, a ritual where depowered mutants face combat to the death to prove worthy of resurrection as powered mutants by the Five.

THE GROVE OF THEORETICAL GATES
Apocalypse has a personal study on Krakoa.

AKADEMOS HABITAT
A collection of biomes that act as homes, schools and training facilities for young mutants.

HOUSE OF X
Charles Xavier resides in the House of X.

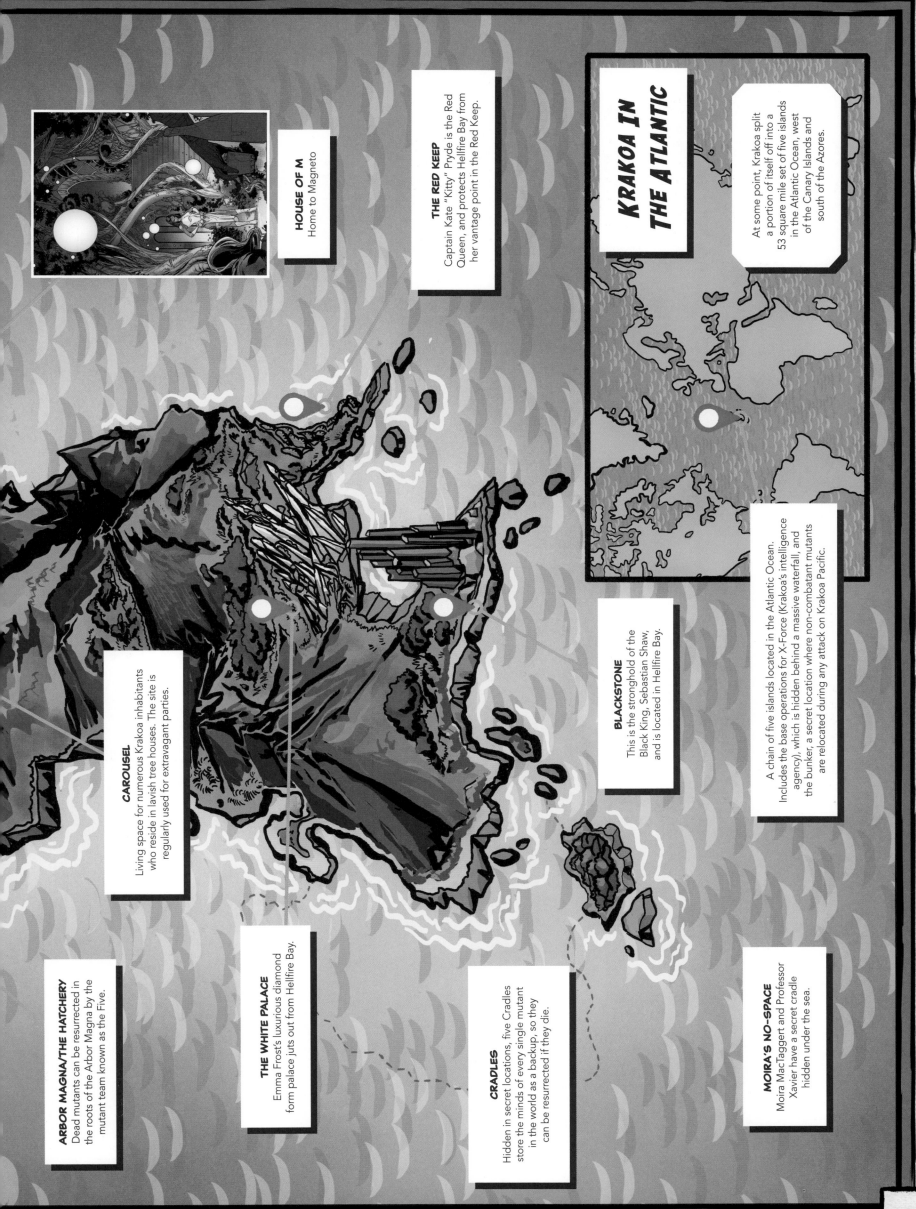

HOUSE OF M
Home to Magneto

THE RED KEEP
Captain Kate "Kitty" Pryde is the Red Queen, and protects Hellfire Bay from her vantage point in the Red Keep.

At some point, Krakoa split a portion of itself into a 53 square mile set of five islands in the Atlantic Ocean, west of the Canary Islands and south of the Azores.

BLACKSTONE
This is the stronghold of the Black King, Sebastian Shaw, and is located in Hellfire Bay.

A chain of five islands located in the Atlantic Ocean. Includes the base operations for X-Force (Krakoa's intelligence agency), which is hidden behind a massive waterfall, and the bunker, a secret location where non-combatant mutants are relocated during any attack on Krakoa Pacific.

CAROUSEL
Living space for numerous Krakoa inhabitants who reside in lavish tree houses. The site is regularly used for extravagant parties.

ARBOR MAGNA/THE HATCHERY
Dead mutants can be resurrected in the roots of the Arbor Magna by the mutant team known as the Five.

THE WHITE PALACE
Emma Frost's luxurious diamond form palace juts out from Hellfire Bay.

CRADLES
Hidden in secret locations, five Cradles store the minds of every single mutant in the world as a backup, so they can be resurrected if they die.

MOIRA'S NO-SPACE
Moira MacTaggert and Professor Xavier have a secret cradle hidden under the sea.

SUBTERRANEA

BENEATH THE SURFACE OF THE EARTH IS A HIDDEN KINGDOM, ONCE THE HOME OF THE DEVIANTS, A RACE CREATED BY THE CELESTIALS. SINCE THEN, MANY DIFFERENT RACES AND PEOPLE HAVE MADE THEIR HOME UNDER THE GROUND. A VAST SERIES OF TUNNELS LINK DIFFERENT UNDERGROUND CITIES TO THE SURFACE WORLD, AND TO MONSTER ISLAND IN THE PACIFIC OCEAN.

SUBTERRANEAN RACES

MOLOIDS
This race of slender, light-averse humanoids were created to be a slave race. In recent times, they were discovered by Mole Man, Harvey Elder, who used them to do his bidding. The Fantastic Four have helped some Moloids become more independent, and four young Moloids have joined the Future Foundation.

LAVA MEN
Once members of the Gortokian slave race created by the Deviants, the Lava Men were mystically transformed by the demon Cha'sa'dra into an angry people made from living molten lava.

LIZARD MEN
The mutated race of Lizard Men have their own society under the Earth.

MONSTERS
Subterranea also links to Monster Island, providing Mole Man with a wide variety of different monsters to use in his war against the surface world.

TYRANNOIDS
Another race created centuries ago by the Deviants, these underground dwellers were discovered by the long-lived conqueror Tyrannus some time after he was banished to Subterranea in the fifth century. He has ruled them ever since.

FOUNTAIN OF YOUTH
Often told about in legend, the Fountain of Youth is hidden many miles beneath the surface of the Earth. Tyrannus used it to keep himself young.

SINISTER LONDON
Mister Sinister harnessed the power of the Dreaming Celestial to create an underground version of 19th-century London, populated by clones of himself and others.

MU
Another ancient civilisation that was lost at the same time as Atlantis, the Kingdom of Mu maintains an uneasy peace with Atlantis.

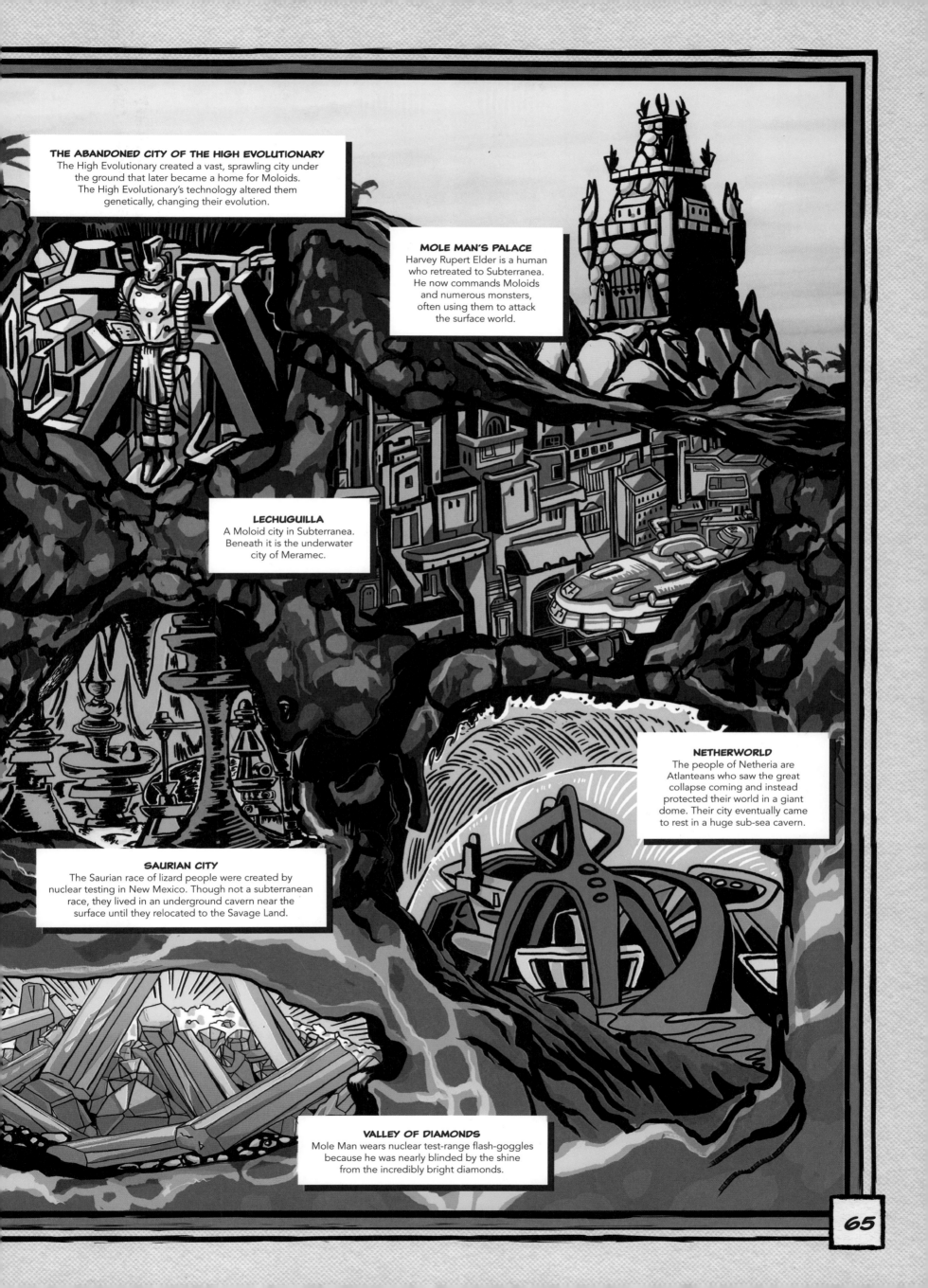

THE ABANDONED CITY OF THE HIGH EVOLUTIONARY
The High Evolutionary created a vast, sprawling city under the ground that later became a home for Moloids. The High Evolutionary's technology altered them genetically, changing their evolution.

MOLE MAN'S PALACE
Harvey Rupert Elder is a human who retreated to Subterranea. He now commands Moloids and numerous monsters, often using them to attack the surface world.

LECHUGUILLA
A Moloid city in Subterranea. Beneath it is the underwater city of Meramec.

NETHERWORLD
The people of Netheria are Atlanteans who saw the great collapse coming and instead protected their world in a giant dome. Their city eventually came to rest in a huge sub-sea cavern.

SAURIAN CITY
The Saurian race of lizard people were created by nuclear testing in New Mexico. Though not a subterranean race, they lived in an underground cavern near the surface until they relocated to the Savage Land.

VALLEY OF DIAMONDS
Mole Man wears nuclear test-range flash-goggles because he was nearly blinded by the shine from the incredibly bright diamonds.

AFRICA

AFRICA IS THE RICHEST CONTINENT IN TERMS OF DIAMONDS, MINERALS AND VIBRANIUM, MEANING THAT IT HAS BECOME A TARGET FOR SUPER VILLAIN ATTACKS FROM ALL OVER THE WORLD. THANKFULLY, AFRICA HAS A SIZEABLE ROSTER OF SUPER HEROES TO PROTECT IT.

KINGDOM OF CANAAN
Arms dealer and super villain Moses Magnum used his personal army to usurp King Baru and place himself as leader, then led campaigns against Wakanda.

NAROBIA
Narobia is an extremely wealthy country due to its natural diamond deposits. Princess Zanda is the ruler of Narobia and uses her country's wealth to fund her lavish lifestyle.

MOHANNDA
The Republic of Mohannda neighbours Wakanda. Black Panther stopped a civil war starting here.

REPUBLIC OF AZANIA
The Apartheid nation of Azania has a superhuman team known as the Supremacists. The Republic of Azania has had many disputes with neighbouring countries, especially Wakanda.

WAKANDA
Wakanda is the most technologically advanced nation on Earth and is protected by the Black Panther.

MBANGAWI
Joshua N'Dingi, better known as Doctor Crocodile, was the ruler of Mbangawi. N'Dingi is rightly distrustful of western countries due to the history of colonialism in his country.

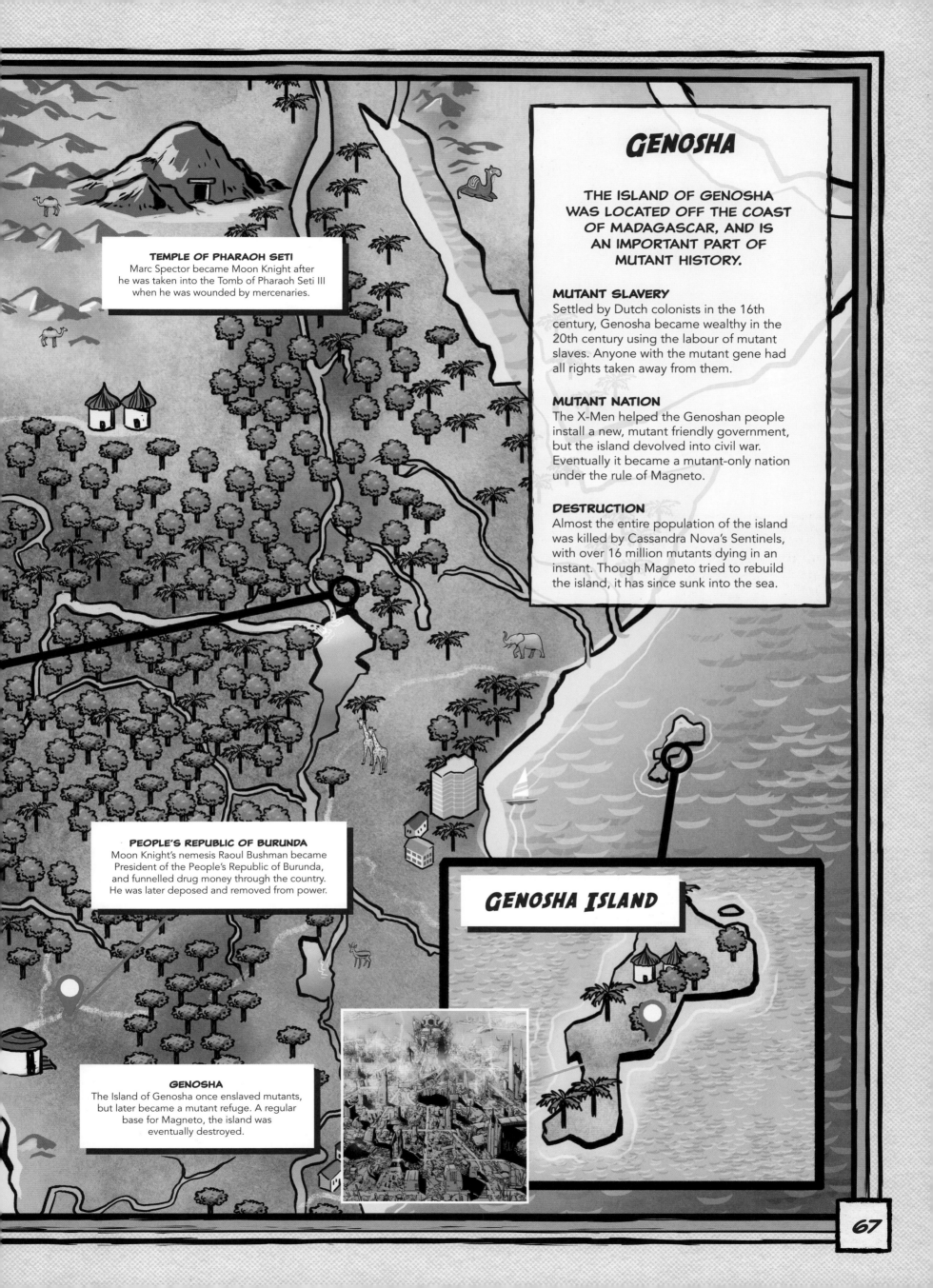

GENOSHA

THE ISLAND OF GENOSHA
WAS LOCATED OFF THE COAST
OF MADAGASCAR, AND IS
AN IMPORTANT PART OF
MUTANT HISTORY.

MUTANT SLAVERY
Settled by Dutch colonists in the 16th century, Genosha became wealthy in the 20th century using the labour of mutant slaves. Anyone with the mutant gene had all rights taken away from them.

MUTANT NATION
The X-Men helped the Genoshan people install a new, mutant friendly government, but the island devolved into civil war. Eventually it became a mutant-only nation under the rule of Magneto.

DESTRUCTION
Almost the entire population of the island was killed by Cassandra Nova's Sentinels, with over 16 million mutants dying in an instant. Though Magneto tried to rebuild the island, it has since sunk into the sea.

TEMPLE OF PHARAOH SETI
Marc Spector became Moon Knight after he was taken into the Tomb of Pharaoh Seti III when he was wounded by mercenaries.

PEOPLE'S REPUBLIC OF BURUNDA
Moon Knight's nemesis Raoul Bushman became President of the People's Republic of Burunda, and funnelled drug money through the country. He was later deposed and removed from power.

GENOSHA ISLAND

GENOSHA
The Island of Genosha once enslaved mutants, but later became a mutant refuge. A regular base for Magneto, the island was eventually destroyed.

WAKANDA

THE KINGDOM OF WAKANDA IS THE MOST TECHNOLOGICALLY ADVANCED NATION IN THE WORLD. VIBRANIUM DEPOSITS FROM AN ANCIENT METEORITE HAVE FUELLED WAKANDAN INVENTIONS FOR CENTURIES. WAKANDA IS RULED BY THE BLACK PANTHER, AND ALTHOUGH WAKANDA IS POWERFUL, IT IS A NATURALLY ISOLATIONIST COUNTRY.

JABARI VILLAGE
The Jabari Lands are in Northern Wakanda. M'Baku leads the White Gorilla cult from Jabari Lands and has challenged T'Challa for leadership of Wakanda more than once.

BIRNIN ZANA – THE GOLDEN CITY
The bright and shining capital city of Wakanda is one of the most advanced places on Earth. It holds the Royal Palace of Wakanda and is the home of the Black Panther.

NECROPOLIS
The Wakandan City of the Dead is where Black Panthers go to die. Black Panther is King of the Dead, giving him the strength and knowledge of every Black Panther who has ever lived.

BIRNIN T'CHAKA
The North of Wakanda is protected by Birnin T'Chaka, which is named after T'Challa's father T'Chaka.

BIRNIN DJATA
Birnin Djata is a city in Wakanda that was named after former Black Panther and Wakandan King Djata.

BIRNIN BASHENGA
Birnin Bashenga is another city named after a former Black Panther and Wakandan King, Bashenga.

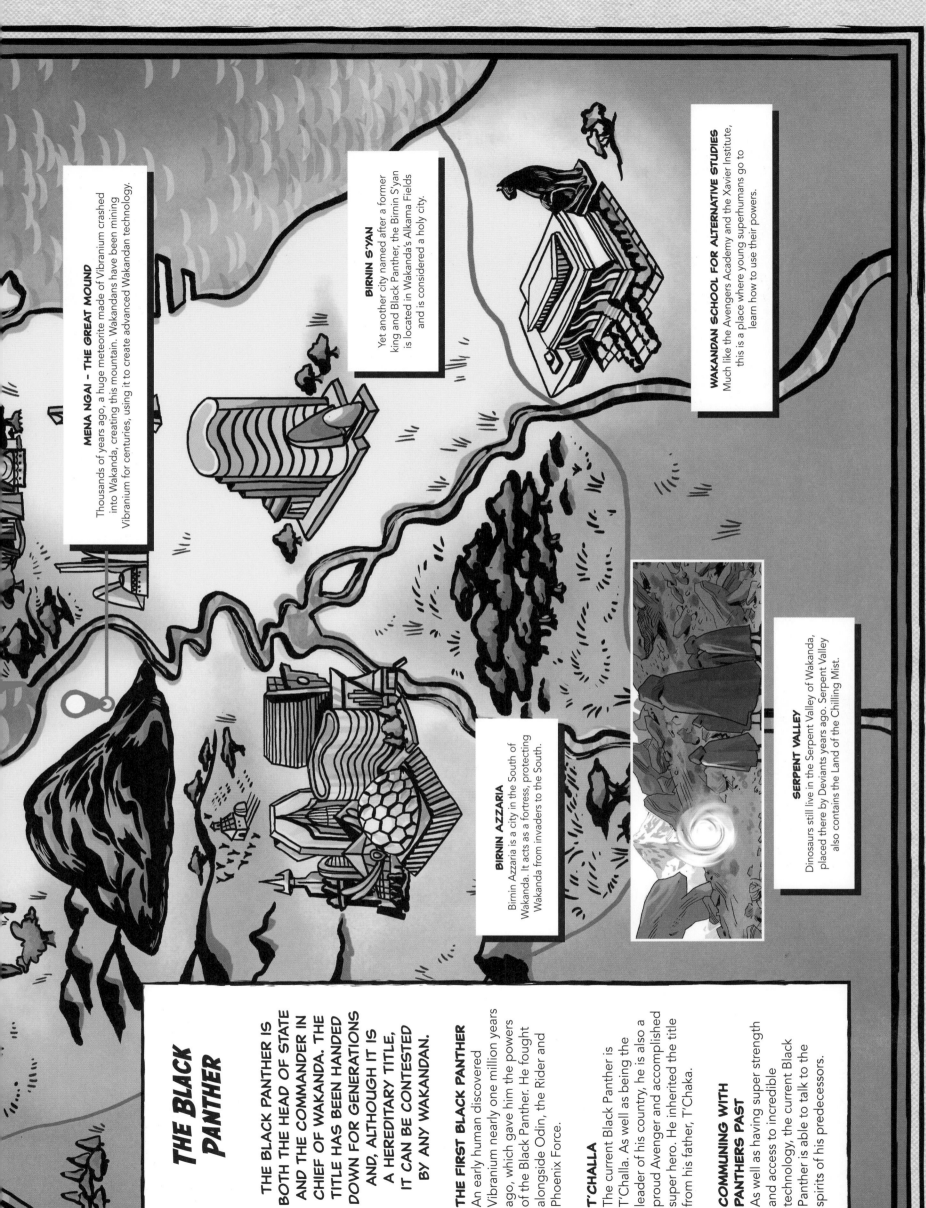

MENA NGAI – THE GREAT MOUND

Thousands of years ago, a huge meteorite made of Vibranium crashed into Wakanda, creating this mountain. Wakandans have been mining Vibranium for centuries, using it to create advanced Wakandan technology.

BIRNIN S'YAN

Yet another city named after a former king and Black Panther, the Birnin S'yan is located in Wakanda's Alkama Fields and is considered a holy city.

WAKANDAN SCHOOL FOR ALTERNATIVE STUDIES

Much like the Avengers Academy and the Xavier Institute, this is a place where young superhumans go to learn how to use their powers.

BIRNIN AZZARIA

Birnin Azzaria is a city in the South of Wakanda. It acts as a fortress, protecting Wakanda from invaders to the South.

SERPENT VALLEY

Dinosaurs still live in the Serpent Valley of Wakanda, placed there by Deviants years ago. Serpent Valley also contains the Land of the Chilling Mist.

THE BLACK PANTHER

THE BLACK PANTHER IS BOTH THE HEAD OF STATE AND THE COMMANDER IN CHIEF OF WAKANDA. THE TITLE HAS BEEN HANDED DOWN FOR GENERATIONS AND, ALTHOUGH IT IS A HEREDITARY TITLE, IT CAN BE CONTESTED BY ANY WAKANDAN.

THE FIRST BLACK PANTHER

An early human discovered Vibranium nearly one million years ago, which gave him the powers of the Black Panther. He fought alongside Odin, the Rider and Phoenix Force.

T'CHALLA

The current Black Panther is T'Challa. As well as being the leader of his country, he is also a proud Avenger and accomplished super hero. He inherited the title from his father, T'Chaka.

COMMUNING WITH PANTHERS PAST

As well as having super strength and access to incredible technology, the current Black Panther is able to talk to the spirits of his predecessors.

NEAR EARTH ORBIT

THE SPACE DIRECTLY ORBITING THE EARTH IS USEFUL FOR SUPER HEROES LOOKING FOR FIRST SIGNS OF INVADING FORCES AND FOR SUPER VILLAINS WHO ARE EVADING PUNISHMENT FOR THEIR CRIMES ON EARTH. INVENTORS LIKE TONY STARK SOMETIMES USE THE ISOLATION OF SPACE AS SECURITY FOR THEIR MORE DANGEROUS EXPERIMENTS.

FOUNDATION
Reed Richards built the Foundation Space Station to maintain geosynchronous orbit directly above the Baxter Building. It is an education and research facility.

PANDORA'S BOX
S.W.O.R.D. has an orbital research station called Pandora's Box where the most dangerous and difficult research is carried out.

THE PEAK VII
The government organisation S.W.O.R.D. is the extraterrestrial equivalent of S.H.I.E.L.D. Their orbital headquarters is known as the Peak.

ALPHA FLIGHT LOW-ORBIT SPACE STATION
Captain Marvel's Alpha Flight space team has been based in orbit above the Earth. This space station has state of the art facilities which included everything from science labs to a working spa.

ASTEROID M
Magneto has had several orbital space bases, all of which were called Asteroid M. The mutant city of Utopia was built from the remains of the first Asteroid M, which crashed off the coast of San Francisco.

STARK SPACE STATION
Costing over 500 million dollars, this was one of Tony Stark's crowning achievements. The space station is solar powered but has a nuclear reactor as a backup.

S.H.I.E.L.D. SPACE STATION
Despite being an expensive project, the S.H.I.E.L.D. Space Station was abandoned and taken over by anti-mutant activists, but later reclaimed by S.H.I.E.L.D.

S.W.O.R.D.

S.W.O.R.D. IS THE ACRONYM FOR THE SENTIENT WORLD OBSERVATION AND RESPONSE DEPARTMENT, A GOVERNMENT AGENCY THAT EXISTS TO MONITOR AND HANDLE EXTRATERRESTRIAL AFFAIRS.

ABIGAIL BRAND
With an alien father and an Earth mother, Abigail Brand is uniquely suited to lead S.W.O.R.D. She is a skilled leader and has the ability to create flames from her hands.

ALPHA FLIGHT
After several attempted alien invasions of Earth, Alpha Flight has become Earth's first line of defence against extraterrestrial threats.

GRAYMALKIN/AVALON
When Cable travelled back in time to the present day, he brought his space station, Graymalkin, with him. Magneto later stole the space station, renaming it Avalon. It was destroyed in a battle, but pieces of it were later used by Cable to create the island Providence.

EARTH'S MOON

EARTH'S MOON HAS BEEN INHABITED FOR MILLIONS OF YEARS, AND HAS LARGE SECTIONS THAT HAVE AIR THAT IS BREATHABLE BY HUMANS. THE WATCHER LIVED ON THE MOON FOR YEARS, USING IT AS A VANTAGE POINT FROM WHICH TO VIEW HUMAN HISTORY. THE X-MEN HAVE A HOUSE ON THE MOON, WITH A ROOM FOR EVERY MEMBER OF CYCLOPS' FAMILY.

BLUE CITY
The Blue City takes up most of the Blue Area of the Moon. It was created by Kree and later abandoned, leaving a vast city of alien ruins on the Moon.

ATTILAN
The Inhuman City of Attilan was moved to the Moon from the Himalayas when the pollution on Earth became too much for the Inhumans to take.

WATCHER'S CITADEL
Uatu the Watcher observed the Earth from his base on the Moon for years. He was killed by Nick Fury Sr. Fury took Uatu's place on the Moon, and now watches mankind as The Unseen.

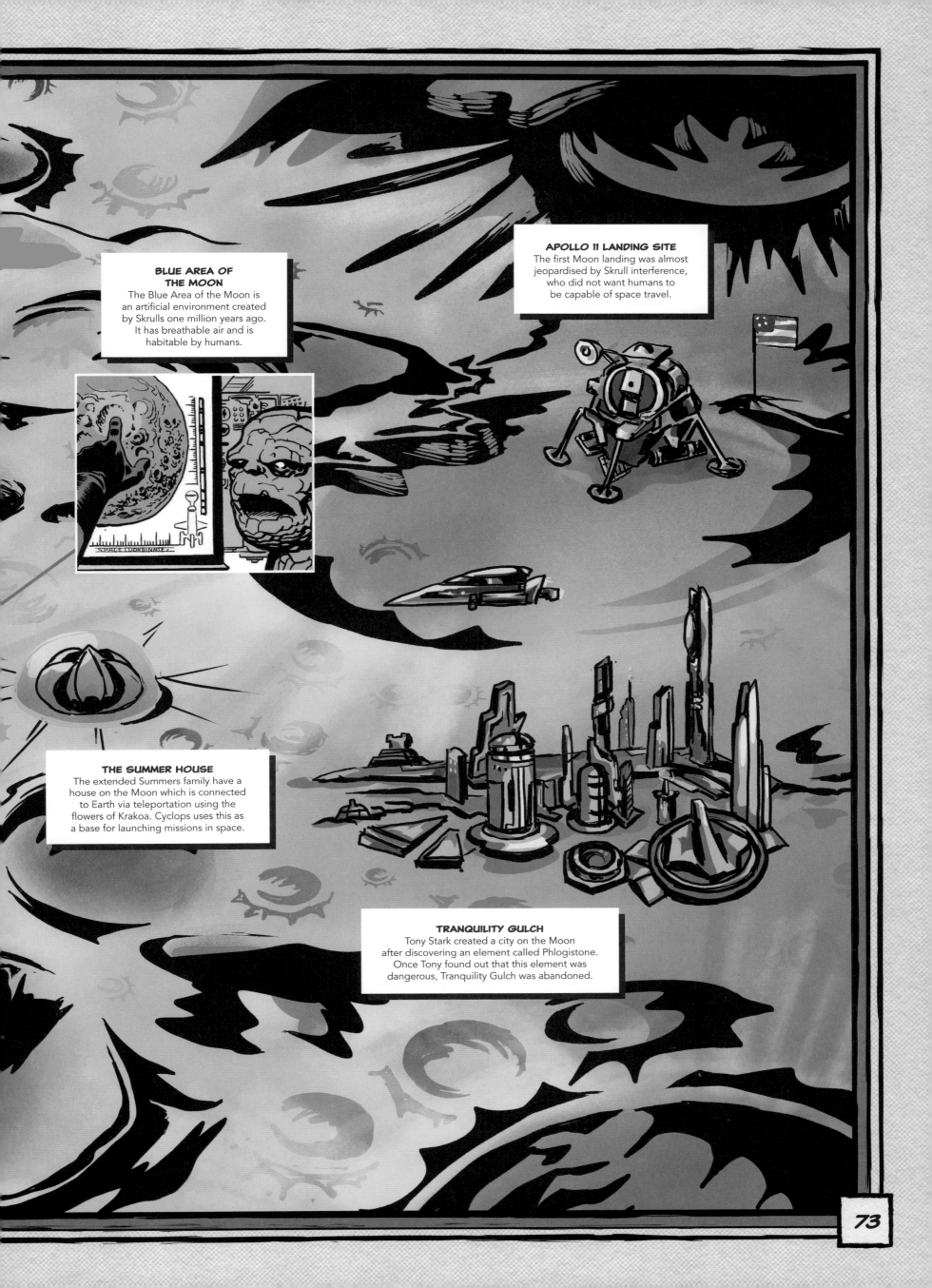

BLUE AREA OF THE MOON
The Blue Area of the Moon is an artificial environment created by Skrulls one million years ago. It has breathable air and is habitable by humans.

APOLLO 11 LANDING SITE
The first Moon landing was almost jeopardised by Skrull interference, who did not want humans to be capable of space travel.

THE SUMMER HOUSE
The extended Summers family have a house on the Moon which is connected to Earth via teleportation using the flowers of Krakoa. Cyclops uses this as a base for launching missions in space.

TRANQUILITY GULCH
Tony Stark created a city on the Moon after discovering an element called Phlogistone. Once Tony found out that this element was dangerous, Tranquility Gulch was abandoned.

THE SOLAR SYSTEM

FOUND IN THE MILKY WAY GALAXY, OUR SOLAR SYSTEM IS PACKED WITH MANY DIFFERENT TYPES OF INTELLIGENT LIFE. ALTHOUGH MANY COSMIC EVENTS SEEM TO CENTRE AROUND THE EARTH, IT'S SATURN'S MOON OF TITAN THAT PRODUCED THANOS, THE BIGGEST EVER THREAT TO ALL LIFE IN THE UNIVERSE.

TITAN
Thanos was born on Titan, one of the moons of Saturn. Thanos destroyed a huge amount of his homeworld at a young age, starting him on his genocidal path.

SATURN
Kronans from the planet Ria used Saturn as their base, claiming to be Stone Men from Saturn. They were stopped in their invasion of Earth by Thor.

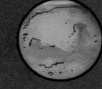

VENUS
Several alien races have claimed to be from Venus.

MARS
Martians have been travelling to Earth for centuries, sometimes peacefully but often as an invading force. Recently, Ex Nihilo has transformed the surface of Mars, making it habitable and verdant.

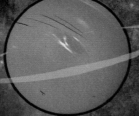

NEPTUNE
So far there is no recorded life on Neptune.

URANUS
Uranus is the home of the two species of Uranians. Human Robert Grayson was sent to the planet Uranus as a child, where he was given incredible powers. He returned to Earth and took on the super hero identity of Marvel Boy.

JUPITER
The fifth planet from the Sun could become an Earth colony, according to the timeline of the Guardians of the Galaxy's 31st century.

THE SUN
The star at the centre of our solar system gives power to everything in it.

MERCURY
Mercury is apparently uninhabited.

EARTH
The Earth is famous throughout the galaxy as being the home of legendary heroes.

THE ORCHIS FORGE
Scientists that had left organisations including S.H.I.E.L.D., S.W.O.R.D., Hydra and A.I.M. came together to stop what they saw as the mutant threat. The Orchis Forge was designed to create a Mother Mold, which would create Master Molds, which would in turn create new Sentinels.

THE TEN REALMS

THE TEN REALMS OF ASGARD WERE KNOWN AS THE NINE REALMS, BEFORE IT WAS DISCOVERED THAT ODIN HAD CUT OFF LINKS TO THE TENTH REALM, HEVEN. THERE ARE MANY LINKS BETWEEN THE REALMS AS SEVERAL OF THE REALMS ARE ON THE SAME PLANE, AND ASGARD, ALFHEIM, NIDAVELLIR AND VANAHEIM ARE ALL ON THE SAME CONTINENT.

VANAHEIM
The Vanir, also known as the Wise Gods of Old, live in Vanaheim. The Vanir and Asgardians are both Aesir as they are descended from common ancestors.

YGGDRASILL
Yggdrasill the world tree contains all of creation.

MIDGARD
Earth, where the humans live. Asgardians have been travelling to Midgard for centuries.

ALFHEIM
The home of the peaceful light elves, allies of Asgard. Their capital city of Alfheim is Ljosalfgard.

HEL/NIFLHEIM
Those who have died without honour go to Hel, which is ruled over by Hela, Queen of the Dead.

SVARTALFHEIM
Dark elves reside in Svartalfheim. Malekith the Accursed has led his tribe of dark elves in bloody wars against other realms and other dark elves.

HEVEN
This paradise realm of angels was once at war with Asgard. After the war, Odin cut off all links from Heven to the other Nine Realms, and the realm was only recently rediscovered by Thor and Loki.

NIDAVELLIR
Nidavellir is the home of the dwarves, who live underground and create powerful weapons for their allies.

ASGARD
Thor, Odin and the Asgardians live in the City of Asgard which is the capital of the realm of Asgard. The realm of Asgard also contains Valhalla, realm of the honoured dead.

MUSPELHEIM
Fire demons ruled by the Fire Giant Surtur live in this realm of eternal fire. This land is linked to Niffleheim, the land of ice, by Ginnungagap, the Yawning Void.

JOTUNHEIM
The land of Frost Giants. Thor's adoptive brother Loki is the biological son of King Laufey of Jotunheim.

SOME OF THE DIFFERENT RACES OF THE TEN REALMS

ASGARDIANS
Asgardians look human, but have vastly longer lifespans. They have been travelling between realms for millions of years and were worshipped as Norse gods.

DWARVES
Widely regarded to be expert craftsmen, dwarves have an alliance with Asgard and have made countless magic weapons including Mjölnir and Stormbreaker.

ELVES
The honourable light elves are often at war with the sinister dark elves.

ASGARD

THE CONTINENT OF ASGARD IS SO BIG THAT IT HOLDS FOUR OF THE TEN REALMS. THE HOME OF THOR AND THE ASGARDIANS, THE CITY OF ASGARD HAS SEEN MILLIONS OF YEARS OF BATTLES AND HEROIC DEEDS.

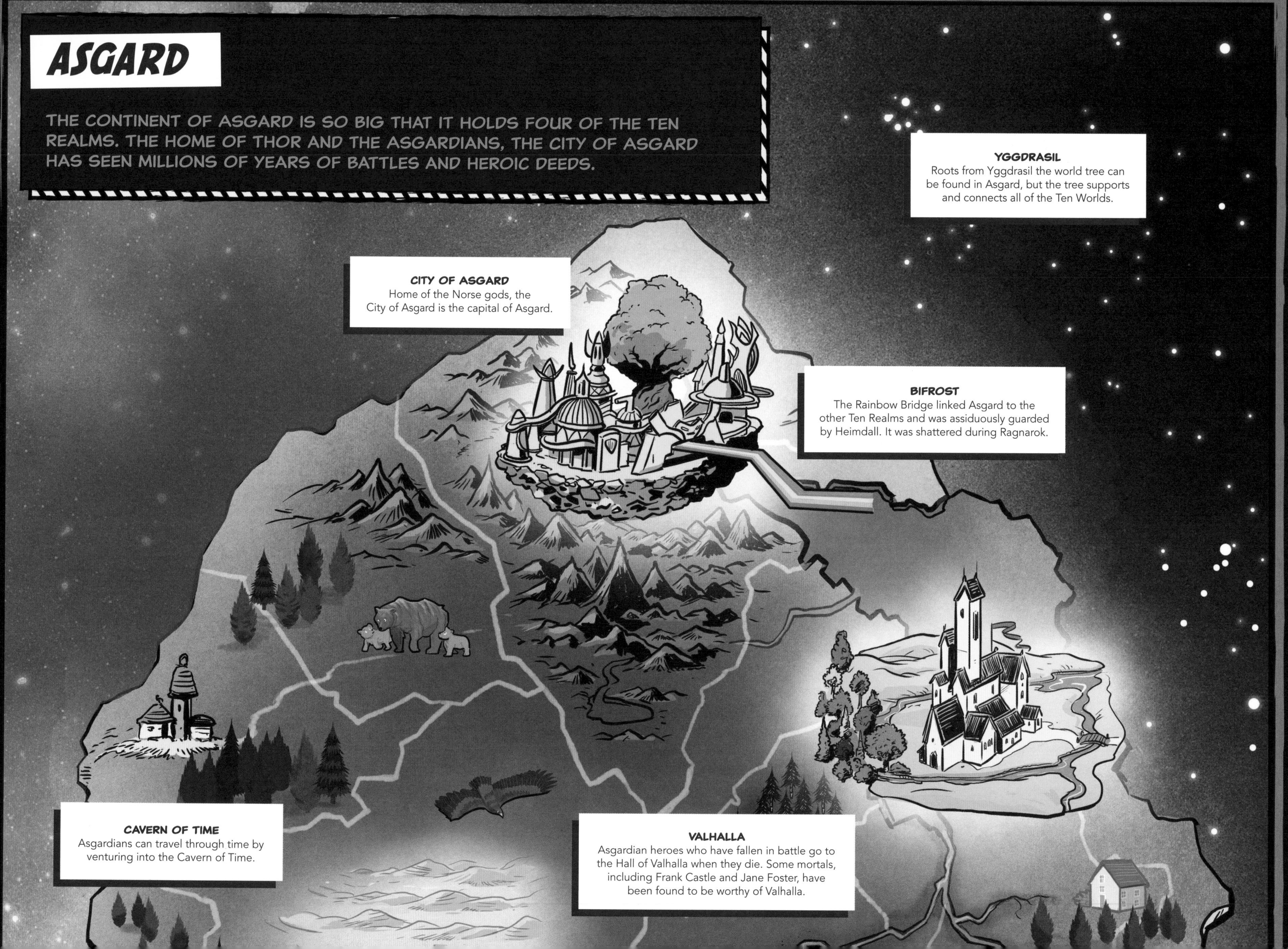

YGGDRASIL

Roots from Yggdrasil the world tree can be found in Asgard, but the tree supports and connects all of the Ten Worlds.

BIFROST

The Rainbow Bridge linked Asgard to the other Ten Realms and was assiduously guarded by Heimdall. It was shattered during Ragnarok.

VALHALLA

Asgardian heroes who have fallen in battle go to the Hall of Valhalla when they die. Some mortals, including Frank Castle and Jane Foster, have been found to be worthy of Valhalla.

CITY OF ASGARD

Home of the Norse gods, the City of Asgard is the capital of Asgard.

CAVERN OF TIME

Asgardians can travel through time by venturing into the Cavern of Time.

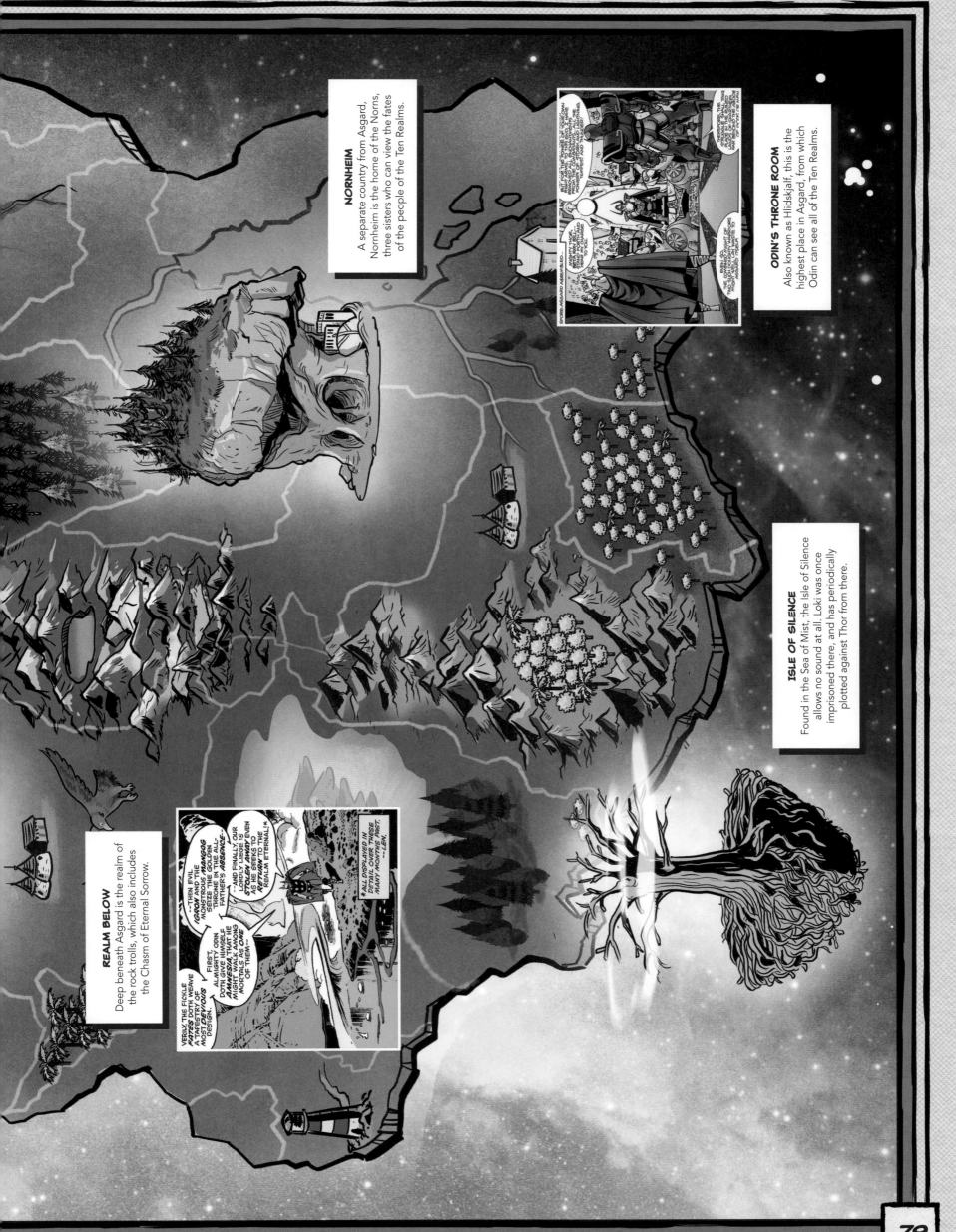

NORNHEIM

A separate country from Asgard, Nornheim is the home of the Norns, three sisters who can view the fates of the people of the Ten Realms.

ODIN'S THRONE ROOM

Also known as Hlidskjalf, this is the highest place in Asgard, from which Odin can see all of the Ten Realms.

ISLE OF SILENCE

Found in the Sea of Mist, the Isle of Silence allows no sound at all. Loki was once imprisoned there, and has periodically plotted against Thor from there.

REALM BELOW

Deep beneath Asgard is the realm of the rock trolls, which also includes the Chasm of Eternal Sorrow.

THOR

THE ASGARDIAN GOD OF THUNDER, THOR IS THE SON OF ODIN, THE ALL-FATHER OF ASGARD, AND GAEA, THE GODDESS OF THE EARTH. ALTHOUGH HE CAN TRAVEL BETWEEN ANY REALM, THOR HAS BEEN DRAWN TO MIDGARD, AND WAS INSTRUMENTAL IN THE FORMING OF THE AVENGERS.

POWERS

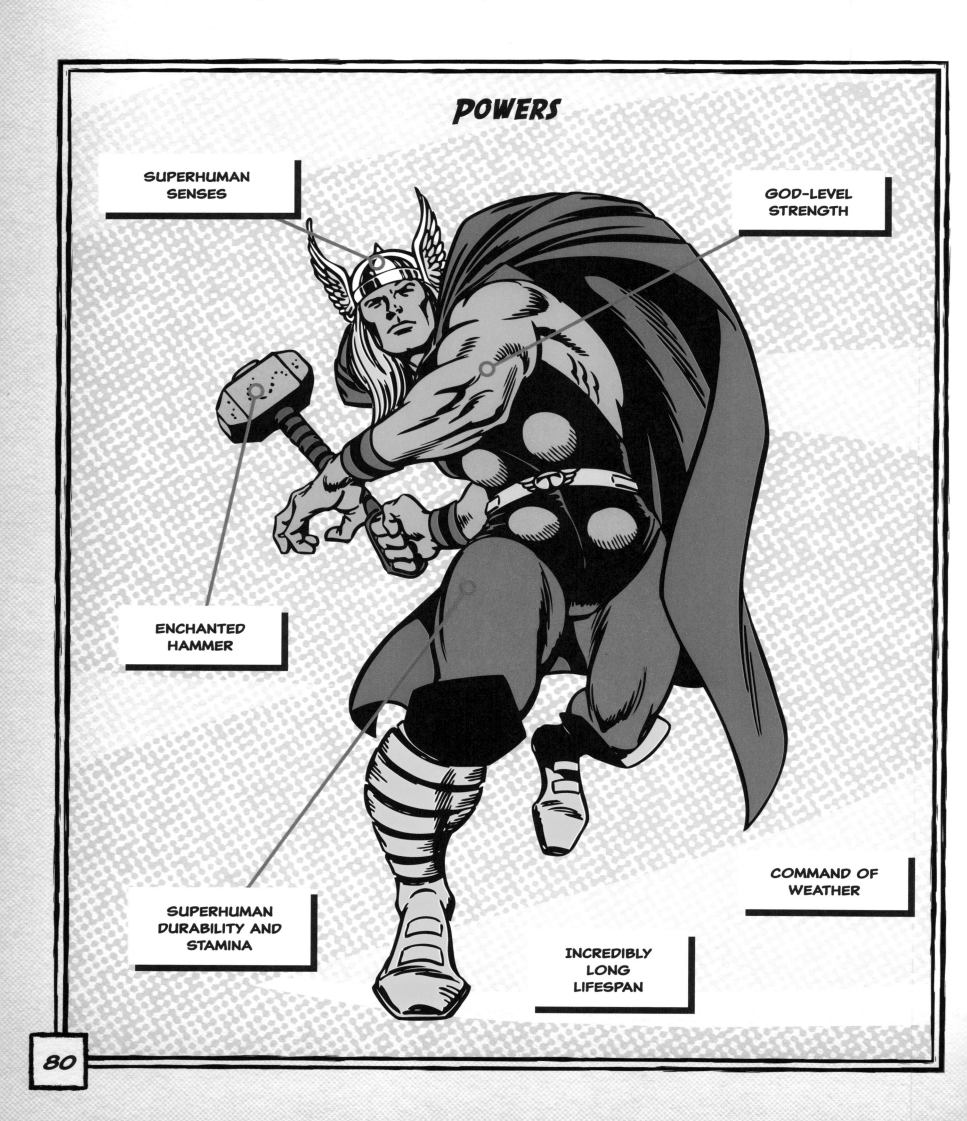

SUPERHUMAN SENSES

GOD-LEVEL STRENGTH

ENCHANTED HAMMER

SUPERHUMAN DURABILITY AND STAMINA

COMMAND OF WEATHER

INCREDIBLY LONG LIFESPAN

THE WORTHY

THOR ODINSON IS NOT THE ONLY PERSON TO HAVE BEEN DEEMED WORTHY ENOUGH TO WIELD THE ENCHANTED HAMMER MJÖLNIR.

BETA RAY BILL
A genetically modified alien from a dead galaxy, Bill was able to pick up Mjölnir in a fight, imbuing him with the power of Thor. Odin has since given him his own hammer, Stormbreaker.

CAPTAIN AMERICA
Steve Rogers was able to wield Thor's hammer during a battle against magic forces.

THUNDERSTRIKE
Eric Masterson was a human who had the power of Thor while Thor Odinson was missing. He later became the hero Thunderstrike, using an enchanted mace.

THOR, THE GODDESS OF THUNDER
Jane Foster picked up Mjölnir and became Thor, the Goddess of Thunder, when Thor Odinson was briefly unworthy of the title.

ASGARD AND BEYOND

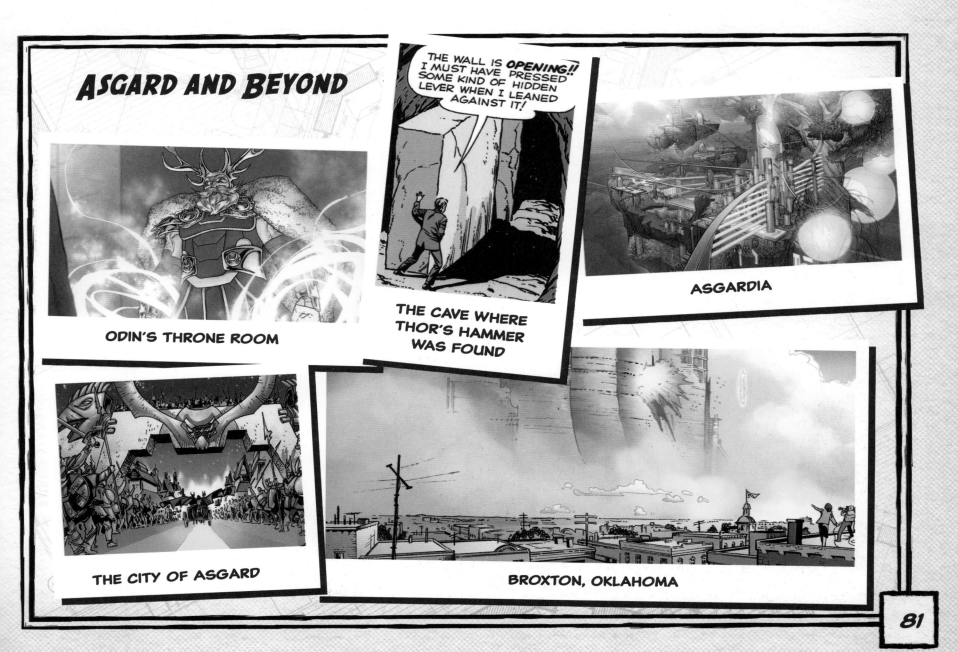

THE WALL IS **OPENING!!** I MUST HAVE PRESSED SOME KIND OF HIDDEN LEVER WHEN I LEANED AGAINST IT!

ODIN'S THRONE ROOM

THE CAVE WHERE THOR'S HAMMER WAS FOUND

ASGARDIA

THE CITY OF ASGARD

BROXTON, OKLAHOMA

THE UNIVERSE

THE UNIVERSE CONTAINS OVER ONE HUNDRED BILLION GALAXIES. THESE ARE THE KEY GALAXIES IN OUR SECTION OF THE UNIVERSE. THOUGH THEY HAVE DEVELOPED AND EVOLVED IN DIFFERENT WAYS, WARS BETWEEN GALAXIES ARE THE ONE CONSTANT.

ANDROMEDA GALAXY
The sprawling Skrull Empire is made up of 1,000 worlds, all ruled by a single Emperor. The warlike Skrull Empire is always expanding and has its sights set on all the other galaxies in the universe. Klyntar, the planet of the symbiotes, and birthplace of Venom, is in the Andromeda Galaxy.

THE FAULT
The Fault is a giant rift in the middle of the universe that allows access to different, alternate universes.

SHI'AR GALAXY
The Shi'ar Empire is vast and expansionist. As well as the Shi'ar, this galaxy also contains the Spartoi, ruled by J'son of Sparta, Star Lord's father.

THE BLACK GALAXY
Ego the living planet was born in the Black Galaxy, a dark and mysterious galaxy far away from the Milky Way. The Black Galaxy was later destroyed giving birth to a Celestial.

THE INTERGALACTIC EMPIRE OF WAKANDA
Wakandan astronauts were thrown through time and space into a new system of Galaxies which they named the Intergalactic Empire of Wakanda. The Benhazin System contained an asteroid belt made of Vibranium, which was used to build this empire.

DIFFERENT ALIEN RACES

KREE

SKRULL

CHITAURI

CELESTIAL

KLYNTAR

SHI'AR

WATCHER

SAKARRAN

BROOD

THE MILKY WAY
Earth, Titan and Alpha Centauri are all in the Milky Way galaxy. A large concentration of super powered beings are located here, and many intergalactic events have taken place in the Milky Way.

GREATER MAGELLANIC CLOUD
For generations the Kree Empire was ruled by an AI called the Supreme Intelligence, but this was destroyed in the Kree/Shi'ar War. Hala is the centre of the Kree Empire.

FORNAX
Fornax contains the Great Portal, a wormhole which connects to other wormholes all over the universe. The Great Portal is close to Sakaar in the Tayo star system.

THE GUARDIANS OF THE GALAXY

TWO DIFFERENT TEAMS HAVE TAKEN THE NAME GUARDIANS OF THE GALAXY. ONE WAS CREATED BY STAR-LORD IN THE PRESENT DAY, AS A TEAM OF INTERGALACTIC HEROES AND MISFITS. THE OTHER TEAM COMES FROM AN ALTERNATE FUTURE, WHERE ALIENS HAVE ENSLAVED THE EARTH IN THE 31ST CENTURY.

STAR LORD'S TEAM

STAR-LORD

DRAX

GAMORA

GROOT

ROCKET

MANTIS

IRON MAN

ANGELA

CAPTAIN MARVEL

AGENT VENOM

KITTY PRYDE

THING

ANT-MAN

NOVA

HERCULES

31ST CENTURY TEAM

CHARLIE-27

MAJOR VICTORY

MARTINEX

YONDU

STARHAWK

NIKKI

ALETA

YELLOWJACKET

KNOWHERE

THE CURRENT DAY GUARDIANS OF THE GALAXY SPENT SOME TIME USING KNOWHERE AS THEIR BASE. KNOWHERE WAS A CITY BUILT IN THE FLOATING HEAD OF A DEAD CELESTIAL. KNOWHERE WAS EVENTUALLY DESTROYED BY THANOS' BLACK ORDER.

THE 31ST CENTURY

THE 31ST CENTURY GUARDIANS COME FROM A DIFFERENT TIMELINE THAN OUR OWN. IN THEIR TIMELINE, MARTIANS INVADED THE EARTH IN 2001, AND THE EARTH WAS INVADED BY THE BADOON IN THE 31ST CENTURY. TIME LOST 20TH CENTURY ASTRONAUT VANCE ASTRO LED THE REBELLION AGAINST THE BADOON WITH HIS TEAM OF GUARDIANS.

SAKAAR

A VIOLENT PLANET ON THE EDGE OF THE FORNAX GALAXY, WHERE THE RELIGIOUS SHADOW PEOPLE SECRETLY CREATED THE GREAT PORTAL, A WORMHOLE THEY HOPED WOULD LEAD THE PROPHESIED BRINGER OF PEACE TO THEIR WORLD. THE RED KING RULED OVER SAKAAR UNTIL THE HULK, KNOWN LOCALLY AS THE GREEN SCAR, LED THE PEOPLE OF SAKAAR IN REVOLT AGAINST HIM.

NORTHERN STEPPES
The home of the Shadow People, who founded the Saka religion, which teaches of two warriors who will both bring peace to and destroy the world.

THE WASTELANDS
Once the centre of Sakaar, this entire area was devastated during the Great Spike War and is now uninhabitable.

OKINI
Once advanced technology was introduced to Sakaar, the Okini province established itself as the Empire's weapons and technology centre.

FILLIA
Fillia was a province which stood up against the tyrannical Red King, and was severely punished for this insurrection.

THE MAW
This gladiator school trained warriors to fight in the Great Arena for the amusement of the people of Sakaar.

THE GREAT ARENA
A weakened Hulk was forced to fight in the Great Arena when he first fell from the Great Portal. He became its champion and was known as the Green Scar.

CROWN CITY
The powerful Red King lived in luxury in the Crown City, while his own people starved in shanty towns all over Sakaar.

THE WARBOUND

HULK FOUGHT IN THE ARENA IN SAKAAR AND FORMED A SPECIAL BOND WITH A NUMBER OF HIS FELLOW WARRIORS. THEY MADE A BATTLE OATH TO EACH OTHER THAT CANNOT BE BROKEN.

KORG
Korg is believed to have been one of the Kronan who attempted an invasion of Earth that was stopped by Thor Odinson. Years later, Korg ended up in the Sakaar arena with Hulk.

NO-NAME
A Brood from Broodworld. No-Name proved undyingly loyal and a great warrior.

CAIERA
The Hulk fell very much in love with Caiera. She was pregnant with their son when she died in an explosion.

MIEK
Sakaar is also home to a native insectoid race. A shunned member of this race, Miek, eventually allowed a damaged warp core drive to explode, which killed Caiera. When Hulk learned that Miek did this in an effort to help Hulk stay focused on destroying, the bond between them was severed.

HIROIM
Once a priest on Sakaar, Hiroim fell out of favour and was eventually enslaved and forced to fight in the arena. He was able to use shadow magic in battle.

DIFFERENT DIMENSIONS

MANY FANTASTIC DIMENSIONS EXIST ALONGSIDE OUR WORLD, EACH WITH BEWILDERINGLY DIFFERENT RULES OF TIME AND SPACE. SKILLED NAVIGATORS SUCH AS STEPHEN STRANGE CAN MOVE BETWEEN DIMENSIONS, BUT NOT EVERY HUMAN MIND IS CAPABLE OF HANDLING THE CHANGE.

THE ASTRAL PLANE
This dimension exists all around us but cannot be seen by normal people, where energy and consciousness are visible. Psychics and sorcerers can leave their physical bodies to navigate the astral plane, and can use it to gain power.

MICROVERSE
The Microverse is accessed by shrinking to a subatomic level (using, for example, Pym Particles) to pass into a parallel dimension. This dimension does not exist within the atoms, but is accessed by passing through them.

OTHERPLACE/LIMBO
Illyana Rasputin, Magik from the X-Men, was trapped in limbo for years. She eventually became ruler of this dimension, but at the cost of a part of her soul.

NEGATIVE ZONE
The Fantastic Four discovered this dimension which is ruled by Annihilus. The Negative Zone is a spare and unforgiving place, and was the origination point of the supremely destructive Annihilation Wave.

THE DARK DIMENSION
Dormammu was banished to the Dark Dimension and now resides there, plotting his takeover of all reality. The Dark Dimension is home of the shambling Mindless Ones.

K'UN LUN
Iron Fist's home of K'un-Lun exists in a different dimension, which can only be visited from our dimension at very specific times.

MEPHISTO'S HELL
Not to be confused with the Asgardian realm of Hel, this dark and fiery place of the dammed is ruled by Mephisto.

THE MULTIVERSE

THE MARVEL UNIVERSE IS ONE OF MANY. IT IS PART OF A WIDER MULTIVERSE, A COLLECTION OF DIFFERENT ALTERNATE UNIVERSES. ALTERNATE UNIVERSES DIVERGE AT KEY POINTS, OFTEN WHEN ONE CHANGE OF EVENTS HAS A MAJOR IMPACT ON HISTORY.

MARVEL NOIR
REALITY-90214
The 1920s and 1930s saw the arrival of heroes to fight organised crime. Prohibition-era versions of Spider-Man, Luke Cage and Daredevil battle mobsters like the Kingpin and Hammerhead.

THE MARVEL UNIVERSE
REALITY-616
Each universe has a designation and number. The universe in the rest of this book is Reality-616.

SQUADRON SUPREME
REALITY-712
The Squadron Supreme was a super hero team that decided the best way to save the world was to rule it. This reality was destroyed and apparently only Hyperion escaped.

HOUSE OF M
REALITY-58163
In this alternate reality, Magneto and his family rule a Mutant Utopia, where mutants have more power than humans. The world is split between different super-powered states, each forming an uneasy truce.

MARVEL 2099
REALITY-928
An alternate future where, by the year 2099, greedy corporations rule the world. A second Age of Heroes, featuring Spider-Man, the X-Men, Doom and the Punisher, among others, takes place in 2099.

1602
REALITY-311
A time-travelling Steve Rogers caused this reality to exist, where the Age of Heroes happened during the time of King James I. Many super powered individuals have fled Europe for the New World.

AGE OF APOCALYPSE
REALITY-295
In this universe, Charles Xavier was killed by the time-travelling Legion before he could found the X-Men. Without Xavier's X-Men to stop him, Apocalypse rules this cruel dystopia.

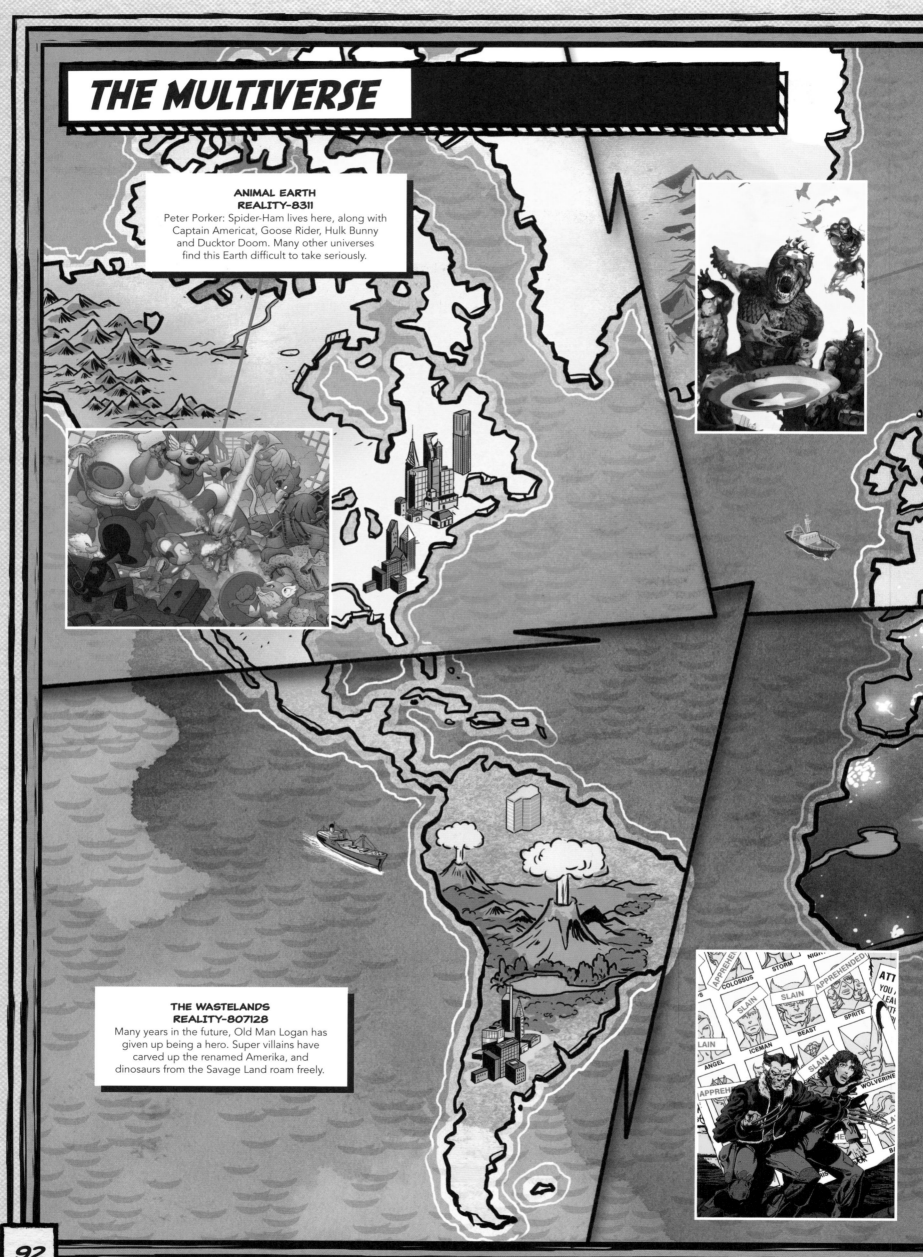

THE MULTIVERSE

**ANIMAL EARTH
REALITY-8311**
Peter Porker: Spider-Ham lives here, along with Captain Americat, Goose Rider, Hulk Bunny and Ducktor Doom. Many other universes find this Earth difficult to take seriously.

**THE WASTELANDS
REALITY-807128**
Many years in the future, Old Man Logan has given up being a hero. Super villains have carved up the renamed Amerika, and dinosaurs from the Savage Land roam freely.

MARVEL ZOMBIES
REALITY-2149
This reality is infected by a zombie plague, spread throughout the universe by infected living-dead super heroes hungry for flesh. These zombies have tried to consume the population of Earth-616 in the past.

THE ULTIMATE UNIVERSE
REALITY-1610
Many heroes in this universe are counterparts of beings in Reality-616. This universe was eventually destroyed when it collided with the main universe. Miles Morales was one of the few heroes to escape.

DAYS OF FUTURE PAST
REALITY-811
Another harsh, dystopian future. Mutants live in concentration camps and are hunted down by Sentinels. An adult Kitty Pryde from this reality has tried to use time travel to prevent this reality from coming to pass.

THE CANCERVERSE
REALITY-10011
Here Mar-Vell killed Death, meaning that nothing could die, spawning a corrupted universe. The Cancerverse needs more room to expand and has tried attacking through the Fault in Reality-616.

BIOGRAPHIES

RALPH MACCHIO

Ralph Macchio spent more than 35 years at Marvel, starting as an assistant editor and later writing for *Avengers*, *Thor* and many others. As editor, he oversaw books across the Marvel line, including shepherding the Ultimate line into existence and editing Stephen King's Marvel adaptations.

Comics seemed to surround Ralph from early in his life. His uncle was DC art legend Wayne Boring, his hometown of Cresskill, New Jersey, doubled as the fictional comic book home of *Ant-Man and the Wasp*, and one of his youthful pastimes was writing letters to his favourite comic books.

After graduating, an encounter with writer Don McGregor at a comic book convention pulled Ralph into Marvel's orbit. Regular visits to the Marvel office ensued, which led to writing assignments for Marvel's in-house fanzine *F.O.O.M.* and by 1976 Ralph was an assistant editor.

Ralph wrote several titles early in his career, most notably *Thor* and *Marvel Two-In-One*, which he co-scripted with Mark Gruenwald, the latter of which included the classic 'Project Pegasus' storyline. He also wrote a six-issue *Solomon Kane* limited series, and teamed up with artist George Perez for the Black Widow 'Web of Intrigue' arc in *Marvel Fanfare*.

Major highlights of his distinguished editorial career include *Daredevil* – particularly Frank Miller's 'Born Again,' *The Man Without Fear and Elektra Lives Again* – Walter Simonson's *Thor*, Doug Moench and Bill Sienkiewicz's *Moon Knight*, righting the Spider-Man franchise from the destabilizing 'Clone Saga,' the launch of the Ultimate Universe, and adaptations of Stephen King's *The Dark Tower and The Stand*.

Ralph Macchio also became well-known for fostering new editors and countless interns, including editor-in-chief Bob Harras and fan favorite artist Joe Madureira. He also kept a spirit of fun alive and well in the Marvel Bullpen through years of practical jokes. Macchio retired from Marvel in 2011 with an editorial tenure second only to Stan Lee.

NED HARTLEY

Ned Hartley is an author and comic writer for both adults and children. He is the writer of *Marvel Origins: Spider-Man*, *Marvel Museum: The Story of the Comics*, *Marvel Heroes and Villains: A Journal by Nick Fury*, *The Ladybird Big Book of Dead Things*, *Paperscapes: The Jungle Book*, multiple *Star Wars* annuals, *Great Lives: Albert Einstein*, *Dark Tales: Hound of the Baskervilles*, *Doctor Who: Choose Your Future Journal* and many more books and comics besides.

Ned writes comics for the *Beano* each week, and has also written for *2000 AD*, *Cor! Buster*, *Monster Fun* and *Wallace and Gromit Comic*. He has contributed to several comics anthologies that will be coming out in the near future.

Ned is also a commissioning editor for Ladybird Books at Penguin Random House, and has worked as an editor for BBC Worldwide, Titan Publishing, Egmont and Immediate Media. He was a magazine editor for many years and worked on a huge range of titles including *Simpsons Comics*, *CBeebies Weekly*, *SpongeBob SquarePants Comics*, *LEGO Star Wars* magazine and others that he can't quite remember right now.

He lives in London with his wife, two children and one cat, and has not been bitten by anything radioactive. Yet.

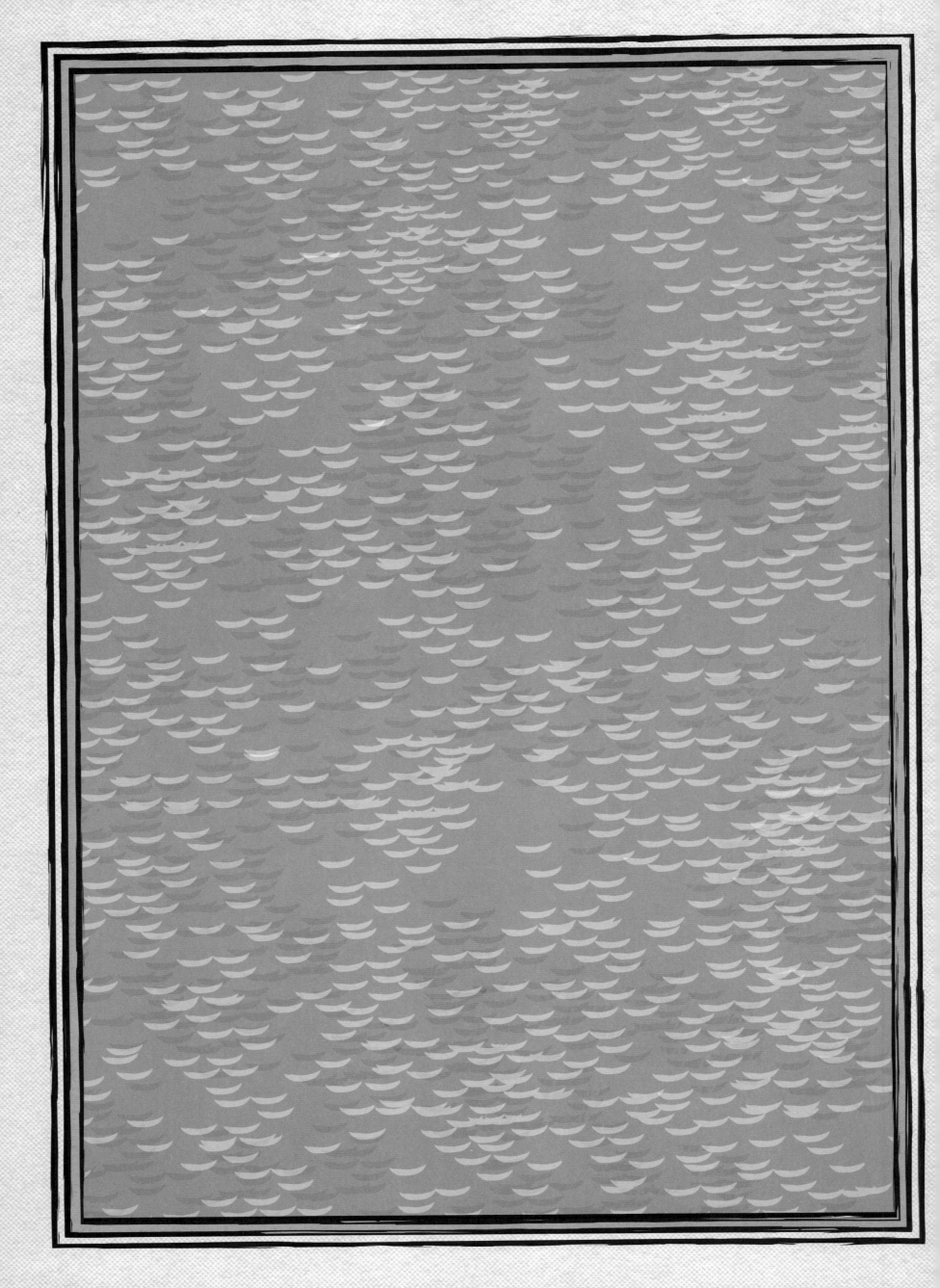